my Yoga Practice

CHRONICLE BOOKS

SAN FRANCISCO

Published exclusively for Target in 2017 by Chronicle Books.

ISBN: 978-1-4521-6264-5

Manufactured in China

Designed by Mia Johnson

The information, practices, and poses in this book are not
offered as medical advice or suggested as treatment
for any condition that might require medical attention.
To avoid injury, practice yoga with a skilled instructor and
consult a health professional to determine your body's
needs and limitations. The writer and publisher hereby
disclaim any liability from injuries resulting from following
any recommendation in this book.

10 9 8 7 6 5 4 3 2 1

Chronicle Books LLC
680 Second Street
San Francisco, California 94107
www.chroniclebooks.com

Contents

About This Journal 5

Before You Begin: My Yoga Profile 6

At-A-Glance Records:

    Yoga Studio Log 8

    Yoga Instructor Log 10

    One-Year Practice Log 12

    For Yoga Moms: My Prenatal Practice 14

    For Yoga Moms: My Postnatal Practice 16

    My Goals 18

Yoga Session Journal 19

Yoga Reference Guide 81

    The Branches of Yoga 82

    Yoga Styles 83

    Illustrated Yoga Pose Directory 88

About This Journal

Self-study is an important part of any yoga practice. Get to know your inner yogi by recording your experiences in the pages of this journal. Whether you have attended only five classes or five hundred; whether you do yoga for health and healing or just for fun; and whether you are committed to one style of yoga or enjoy exploring them all, *My Yoga Practice* will take you deeper into your practice and lead you to enriching self-discoveries, on and off the mat.

Start by turning this page and completing "My Yoga Profile." The next time you do yoga, turn to one of the guided journal entries in the second half of the book and log the details of that session. With space for recording thirty individual sessions, this journal invites you to see how truly dynamic a yoga practice can be. After all, no two yoga sessions are alike. Each is unique, varying not only in pose sequencing, but also in the day-to-day fluctuations of your moods, energy levels, and interests.

Indeed, your yoga practice is a living, ever-evolving entity—just like you. Watch it flourish in these pages as you grow stronger, more balanced, and more present in your daily life.

Namaste.

My Yoga Profile

Complete this profile and share it with your yoga instructors and health coaches who can help you create a customized yoga practice that best meets your needs.

NAME .... TODAY'S DATE .... / .... / ....

CONTACT INFORMATION ....

....

AGE .... WHEN DID YOU FIRST GIVE YOGA A TRY? ....
                                                                        (MONTH)   (YEAR)

DESCRIBE YOUR FIRST IMPRESSIONS OF YOGA ....

....

....

NUMBER OF CLASSES YOU'VE TAKEN IN THE PAST THREE YEARS

☐ 5 OR LESS   ☐ 6-20   ☐ 21-40   ☐ MORE THAN 40

YOUR CURRENT SKILL LEVEL

☐ FIRST-TIMER   ☐ BEGINNER   ☐ ADVANCED BEGINNER   ☐ EARLY INTERMEDIATE   ☐ INTERMEDIATE

☐ ADVANCED INTERMEDIATE   ☐ ADVANCED   ☐ TEACHER-IN-TRAINING   ☐ INSTRUCTOR

WHICH YOGA STYLES HAVE YOU TRIED?

☐ ANUSARA   ☐ ASHTANGA   ☐ BIKRAM   ☐ IYENGAR   ☐ JIVAMUKTI

☐ KRIPALU   ☐ KUNDALINI   ☐ POWER   ☐ RESTORATIVE   ☐ OTHER: ....

WHAT BENEFITS ARE YOU SEEKING IN YOUR YOGA PRACTICE? (CHECK ALL THAT APPLY.)

☐ BODY SCULPTING   ☐ PHYSICAL FITNESS   ☐ FLEXIBILITY   ☐ INCREASED STRENGTH   ☐ IMPROVED BALANCE

☐ STRESS REDUCTION   ☐ ENHANCED SLEEP   ☐ GENERAL HEALTH AND WELL-BEING   ☐ SPIRITUAL ENRICHMENT

☐ OTHER ....   ☐ OTHER ....   ☐ OTHER ....

EMERGENCY CONTACT

NAME .... RELATIONSHIP ....

CONTACT INFORMATION ....

....

Past and current injuries and/or health conditions:

TO RECORD ADDITIONAL INJURIES AND CONDITIONS, TURN TO THE HEALTH TRACKER (PAGES 32-37).

DESCRIBE INJURY/CONDITION ....

.... WHEN DID THE INJURY OCCUR? ....

(MONTH)   (YEAR)

HAVE YOU COMPLETELY RECOVERED?   ☐ YES   ☐ NO

IF YES, WHEN WAS RECOVERY COMPLETE? ....

(MONTH)   (YEAR)

DESCRIBE INJURY/CONDITION ....

.... WHEN DID THE INJURY OCCUR? ....

(MONTH)   (YEAR)

HAVE YOU COMPLETELY RECOVERED?   ☐ YES   ☐ NO

IF YES, WHEN WAS RECOVERY COMPLETE? ....

(MONTH)   (YEAR)

DESCRIBE INJURY/CONDITION ....

.... WHEN DID THE INJURY OCCUR? ....

(MONTH)   (YEAR)

HAVE YOU COMPLETELY RECOVERED?   ☐ YES   ☐ NO

IF YES, WHEN WAS RECOVERY COMPLETE? ....

(MONTH)   (YEAR)

Yoga Studio Log

Record the local studios you've visited, and those you want to visit, to create a helpful log of the yoga centers in your area.

STUDIO NAME

LOCATION

PRIMARY YOGA STYLE

NOTEWORTHY INSTRUCTOR(S)

☐ VISITED ON THESE DATES: **OR** ☐ HAVEN'T BEEN/WANT TO GO

STUDIO NAME

LOCATION

PRIMARY YOGA STYLE

NOTEWORTHY INSTRUCTOR(S)

☐ VISITED ON THESE DATES: **OR** ☐ HAVEN'T BEEN/WANT TO GO

STUDIO NAME

LOCATION

PRIMARY YOGA STYLE

NOTEWORTHY INSTRUCTOR(S)

☐ VISITED ON THESE DATES: **OR** ☐ HAVEN'T BEEN/WANT TO GO

STUDIO NAME

LOCATION

PRIMARY YOGA STYLE

NOTEWORTHY INSTRUCTOR(S)

☐ VISITED ON THESE DATES: **OR** ☐ HAVEN'T BEEN/WANT TO GO

STUDIO NAME

LOCATION

PRIMARY YOGA STYLE

NOTEWORTHY INSTRUCTOR(S)

☐ VISITED ON THESE DATES: **OR** ☐ HAVEN'T BEEN/WANT TO GO

STUDIO NAME

LOCATION

PRIMARY YOGA STYLE

NOTEWORTHY INSTRUCTOR(S)

☐ VISITED ON THESE DATES:

OR

☐ HAVEN'T BEEN/WANT TO GO

STUDIO NAME

LOCATION

PRIMARY YOGA STYLE

NOTEWORTHY INSTRUCTOR(S)

☐ VISITED ON THESE DATES:

OR

☐ HAVEN'T BEEN/WANT TO GO

STUDIO NAME

LOCATION

PRIMARY YOGA STYLE

NOTEWORTHY INSTRUCTOR(S)

☐ VISITED ON THESE DATES:

OR

☐ HAVEN'T BEEN/WANT TO GO

STUDIO NAME

LOCATION

PRIMARY YOGA STYLE

NOTEWORTHY INSTRUCTOR(S)

☐ VISITED ON THESE DATES:

OR

☐ HAVEN'T BEEN/WANT TO GO

STUDIO NAME

LOCATION

PRIMARY YOGA STYLE

NOTEWORTHY INSTRUCTOR(S)

☐ VISITED ON THESE DATES:

OR

☐ HAVEN'T BEEN/WANT TO GO

STUDIO NAME

LOCATION

PRIMARY YOGA STYLE

NOTEWORTHY INSTRUCTOR(S)

☐ VISITED ON THESE DATES:

OR

☐ HAVEN'T BEEN/WANT TO GO

Yoga Instructor Log

Note the characteristics of the instructors you've tried, and explore new instructors throughout your community. Rate each of them according to your personal preferences.

Instructor's name

STUDIO/S WHERE HE/SHE TEACHES

THIS INSTRUCTOR INCORPORATES THE FOLLOWING INTO HIS/HER CLASSES:

☐ INSPIRATIONAL COMMENTARY   ☐ HANDS-ON MODIFICATIONS   ☐ CHANTING   ☐ BREATHING EXERCISES

☐ OTHER:

PACE OF FLOW (CIRCLE ONE):   FAST   MODERATE   SLOW

INSTRUCTOR RATINGS: POSE SEQUENCING: CLARITY OF INSTRUCTION: OVERALL RANKING:
                             A+ A A- B C D F   A+ A A- B C D F   A+ A A- B C D F

NOTES

Instructor's name

STUDIO/S WHERE HE/SHE TEACHES

THIS INSTRUCTOR INCORPORATES THE FOLLOWING INTO HIS/HER CLASSES:

☐ INSPIRATIONAL COMMENTARY   ☐ HANDS-ON MODIFICATIONS   ☐ CHANTING   ☐ BREATHING EXERCISES

☐ OTHER:

PACE OF FLOW (CIRCLE ONE):   FAST   MODERATE   SLOW

INSTRUCTOR RATINGS: POSE SEQUENCING: CLARITY OF INSTRUCTION: OVERALL RANKING:
                             A+ A A- B C D F   A+ A A- B C D F   A+ A A- B C D F

NOTES

Instructor's name ....

STUDIO/S WHERE HE/SHE TEACHES ....

THIS INSTRUCTOR INCORPORATES THE FOLLOWING INTO HIS/HER CLASSES:

☐ INSPIRATIONAL COMMENTARY   ☐ HANDS-ON MODIFICATIONS   ☐ CHANTING   ☐ BREATHING EXERCISES

☐ OTHER: ....

PACE OF FLOW (CIRCLE ONE):   FAST   MODERATE   SLOW

INSTRUCTOR RATINGS: POSE SEQUENCING: CLARITY OF INSTRUCTION: OVERALL RANKING:
A+ A A- B C D F   A+ A A- B C D F   A+ A A- B C D F

NOTES ....

....

Instructor's name ....

STUDIO/S WHERE HE/SHE TEACHES ....

THIS INSTRUCTOR INCORPORATES THE FOLLOWING INTO HIS/HER CLASSES:

☐ INSPIRATIONAL COMMENTARY   ☐ HANDS-ON MODIFICATIONS   ☐ CHANTING   ☐ BREATHING EXERCISES

☐ OTHER: ....

PACE OF FLOW (CIRCLE ONE):   FAST   MODERATE   SLOW

INSTRUCTOR RATINGS: POSE SEQUENCING: CLARITY OF INSTRUCTION: OVERALL RANKING:
A+ A A- B C D F   A+ A A- B C D F   A+ A A- B C D F

NOTES ....

....

Instructor's name ....

STUDIO/S WHERE HE/SHE TEACHES ....

THIS INSTRUCTOR INCORPORATES THE FOLLOWING INTO HIS/HER CLASSES:

☐ INSPIRATIONAL COMMENTARY   ☐ HANDS-ON MODIFICATIONS   ☐ CHANTING   ☐ BREATHING EXERCISES

☐ OTHER: ....

PACE OF FLOW (CIRCLE ONE):   FAST   MODERATE   SLOW

INSTRUCTOR RATINGS: POSE SEQUENCING: CLARITY OF INSTRUCTION: OVERALL RANKING:
A+ A A- B C D F   A+ A A- B C D F   A+ A A- B C D F

NOTES ....

....

One-Year Practice Log

Over the coming twelve-month period, circle the corresponding date every time you practice yoga to create a visual record of how often you practice.

JANUARY

1	2	3	4	5	6	7
8	9	10	11	12	13	14
15	16	17	18	19	20	21
22	23	24	25	26	27	28
29	30	31				

TOTAL SESSIONS:

FEBRUARY

1	2	3	4	5	6	7
8	9	10	11	12	13	14
15	16	17	18	19	20	21
22	23	24	25	26	27	28
29						

TOTAL SESSIONS:

MARCH

1	2	3	4	5	6	7
8	9	10	11	12	13	14
15	16	17	18	19	20	21
22	23	24	25	26	27	28
29	30	31				

TOTAL SESSIONS:

APRIL

1	2	3	4	5	6	7
8	9	10	11	12	13	14
15	16	17	18	19	20	21
22	23	24	25	26	27	28
29	30					

TOTAL SESSIONS:

MAY

1	2	3	4	5	6	7
8	9	10	11	12	13	14
15	16	17	18	19	20	21
22	23	24	25	26	27	28
29	30	31				

TOTAL SESSIONS:

JUNE

1	2	3	4	5	6	7
8	9	10	11	12	13	14
15	16	17	18	19	20	21
22	23	24	25	26	27	28
29	30					

TOTAL SESSIONS:

JULY

1	2	3	4	5	6	7
8	9	10	11	12	13	14
15	16	17	18	19	20	21
22	23	24	25	26	27	28
29	30	31	**TOTAL SESSIONS:**			

AUGUST

1	2	3	4	5	6	7
8	9	10	11	12	13	14
15	16	17	18	19	20	21
22	23	24	25	26	27	28
29	30	31	**TOTAL SESSIONS:**			

SEPTEMBER

1	2	3	4	5	6	7
8	9	10	11	12	13	14
15	16	17	18	19	20	21
22	23	24	25	26	27	28
29	30	**TOTAL SESSIONS:**				

OCTOBER

1	2	3	4	5	6	7
8	9	10	11	12	13	14
15	16	17	18	19	20	21
22	23	24	25	26	27	28
29	30	31	**TOTAL SESSIONS:**			

NOVEMBER

1	2	3	4	5	6	7
8	9	10	11	12	13	14
15	16	17	18	19	20	21
22	23	24	25	26	27	28
29	30	**TOTAL SESSIONS:**				

DECEMBER

1	2	3	4	5	6	7
8	9	10	11	12	13	14
15	16	17	18	19	20	21
22	23	24	25	26	27	28
29	30	31	**TOTAL SESSIONS:**			

 TOTAL NUMBER OF PRACTICE SESSIONS OVER TWELVE-MONTH PERIOD:

For Yoga Moms: My Prenatal Practice

As a supplement to other prenatal care, prenatal yoga can help support your body's changing needs and prepare you for the birth of your baby. Track your practice, and key aspects of your pregnancy, here.

DUE DATE /   /

Important Contacts

CARE PROVIDER

CONTACT INFO

□ **DOCTOR** □ **MIDWIFE** □ **DOULA** □ **OTHER** ....

OTHER SUPPORT PROVIDER

CONTACT INFO

□ **DOCTOR** □ **MIDWIFE** □ **DOULA** □ **OTHER** ....

HAVE ANY EXERCISE-RELATED RESTRICTIONS OR PRECAUTIONS BEEN ADVISED BY YOUR CARE PROVIDERS?

□ YES □ NO   **IF YES, LIST THEM HERE** ....

Pregnancy Symptoms

CHECK OFF THE SYMPTOMS YOU'VE HAD IN YOUR FIRST, SECOND, AND THIRD TRIMESTER AND ASK YOUR INSTRUCTOR FOR SPECIFIC POSES THAT ARE RECOMMENDED FOR SYMPTOM RELIEF.

	1ST	2ND	3RD	RECOMMENDED POSE
NAUSEA				
FATIGUE				
INDIGESTION				
ANXIETY				
INSOMNIA				
BACKACHES				
HEADACHES				
OTHER				
OTHER				

FAVORITE PRENATAL YOGA POSES

1. ....
2. ....
3. ....

POSES YOU MIGHT USE DURING CHILDBIRTH

1. ....
2. ....
3. ....

Prenatal Practice Log
RECORD THE DETAILS OF EACH PRENATAL YOGA SESSION.

DATE   /   /   TIME   -

LOCATION

INSTRUCTOR

NOTES

DATE   /   /   TIME   -

LOCATION

INSTRUCTOR

NOTES

DATE   /   /   TIME   -

LOCATION

INSTRUCTOR

NOTES

DATE   /   /   TIME   -

LOCATION

INSTRUCTOR

NOTES

DATE   /   /   TIME   -

LOCATION

INSTRUCTOR

NOTES

DATE   /   /   TIME   -

LOCATION

INSTRUCTOR

NOTES

DATE   /   /   TIME   -

LOCATION

INSTRUCTOR

NOTES

DATE   /   /   TIME   -

LOCATION

INSTRUCTOR

NOTES

DATE   /   /   TIME   -

LOCATION

INSTRUCTOR

NOTES

DATE   /   /   TIME   -

LOCATION

INSTRUCTOR

NOTES

For Yoga Moms: My Postnatal Practice

Return to this section after the birth of your baby and track your postnatal practice. *Note: Medical professionals recommend waiting at least six weeks before attempting any form of physical exercise. Consult your health care provider before resuming or starting a yoga practice.*

NAME OF YOUR BABY

BIRTH DATE

Postnatal Practice Log

DATE / / **TIME** START - FINISH

LOCATION

INSTRUCTOR

NOTES

DATE / / **TIME** START - FINISH

LOCATION

INSTRUCTOR

NOTES

DATE / / **TIME** START - FINISH

LOCATION

INSTRUCTOR

NOTES

DATE / / **TIME** START - FINISH

LOCATION

INSTRUCTOR

NOTES

DATE / / **TIME** START - FINISH

LOCATION

INSTRUCTOR

NOTES

DATE / / **TIME** START - FINISH

LOCATION

INSTRUCTOR

NOTES

DATE / /   **TIME** START - FINISH

LOCATION

INSTRUCTOR

NOTES

DATE / /   **TIME** START - FINISH

LOCATION

INSTRUCTOR

NOTES

DATE / /   **TIME** START - FINISH

LOCATION

INSTRUCTOR

NOTES

DATE / /   **TIME** START - FINISH

LOCATION

INSTRUCTOR

NOTES

DATE / /   **TIME** START - FINISH

LOCATION

INSTRUCTOR

NOTES

DATE / /   **TIME** START - FINISH

LOCATION

INSTRUCTOR

NOTES

DATE / /   **TIME** START - FINISH

LOCATION

INSTRUCTOR

NOTES

DATE / /   **TIME** START - FINISH

LOCATION

INSTRUCTOR

NOTES

My Goals

List your goals (short-term and long-term, yoga-related or not) for an inspirational record of the ways you aim to reach your potential, on and off the mat.

1.

2.

3.

4.

5.

6.

7.

8.

9.

10.

11.

12.

Yoga Session Journal

Record the details of thirty
individual yoga sessions
in the pages ahead and
witness the deepening of
your practice.

Yoga Session ①

DATE   /   /   TIME   START - FINISH

☐ Group Class Practice

NAME OF STUDIO:

NAME OF TEACHER:

TEACHER RATING (CIRCLE ONE): A+ A A- B C D F

CLASS LEVEL:

☐ BEGINNER   ☐ INTERMEDIATE   ☐ ADVANCED

CROWD LEVEL: ① ② ③ ④ ⑤
              NOT CROWDED ▸ CROWDED

TEMPERATURE: ☐ HEATED   ☐ UNHEATED

OR

☐ Home Practice and/or Private Instruction

IN WHAT ROOM/SPACE DID YOU PRACTICE?

ON WHAT PART OF THE BODY DID YOU FOCUS DURING THIS SESSION?

☐ ABDOMINALS   ☐ HIPS
☐ BACK   ☐ BUTTOCKS
☐ SHOULDERS   ☐ LEGS
☐ ARMS   ☐ ANKLES/FEET
☐ WRISTS/HANDS   ☐ OTHER:

Session Details

WHAT STYLE DID YOU PRACTICE DURING THIS SESSION?

☐ ANUSARA   ☐ KRIPALU
☐ ASHTANGA   ☐ KUNDALINI
☐ BIKRAM   ☐ POWER
☐ IYENGAR   ☐ RESTORATIVE
☐ JIVAMUKTI   ☐ VINIYOGA
                 ☐ OTHER:

WHAT TOOLS DID YOU HAVE ON HAND?

☐ MAT   ☐ STRAP
☐ WATER BOTTLE   ☐ BLANKET
☐ TOWEL   ☐ BOLSTER PILLOW
☐ BLOCK   ☐ OTHER:

SOUND ACCOMPANIMENT: ☐ NO MUSIC   ☐ MUSIC

FAVORITE TRACK FROM TODAY'S SESSION
(TURN TO PAGE 20 AND ADD THE SONG TO YOUR YOGA SOUNDTRACK.)

Overall Session Rating

PACE OF FLOW: ① ② ③ ④ ⑤

DYNAMISM OF SEQUENCING: ① ② ③ ④ ⑤

DIFFICULTY: ① ② ③ ④ ⑤

POSES INCLUDED IN TODAY'S SEQUENCING:

☐ STANDING POSES   ☐ FORWARD BENDS
☐ BALANCING POSES   ☐ BACKBENDS
☐ SEATED POSES   ☐ INVERSIONS
☐ ABDOMINAL   ☐ RESTING POSES
  STRENGTHENERS
☐ TWISTS

FAVORITE POSE OF TODAY'S SESSION:

MOST CHALLENGING POSE:

POSE YOU HADN'T TRIED BEFORE TODAY:

POSE IN WHICH YOU SHOWED THE MOST IMPROVEMENT:

POSE YOU'D LIKE TO WORK ON IN THE NEXT SESSION:

Dedication

Notes and Takeaways

Self-Review

One a scale of 1 to 5 (low to high), rate the following areas of your performance during this session:

FOCUS: ① ② ③ ④ ⑤

EVENNESS OF BREATH: ① ② ③ ④ ⑤

BALANCE: ① ② ③ ④ ⑤

STRENGTH: ① ② ③ ④ ⑤

ENERGY LEVEL: ① ② ③ ④ ⑤

ATTITUDE: ① ② ③ ④ ⑤

DATE   /   /   TIME start - finish

☐ **Group Class Practice**   ☐ **Home Practice and/or Private Instruction**

NAME OF STUDIO: _____   (OR)   IN WHAT ROOM/SPACE DID YOU PRACTICE?

NAME OF TEACHER: _____

TEACHER RATING (CIRCLE ONE): A+ A A- B C D F

CLASS LEVEL:
☐ BEGINNER ☐ INTERMEDIATE ☐ ADVANCED

CROWD LEVEL: ① ② ③ ④ ⑤
NOT CROWDED → CROWDED

TEMPERATURE: ☐ HEATED ☐ UNHEATED

ON WHAT PART OF THE BODY DID YOU FOCUS DURING THIS SESSION?

☐ ABDOMINALS   ☐ HIPS
☐ BACK   ☐ BUTTOCKS
☐ SHOULDERS   ☐ LEGS
☐ ARMS   ☐ ANKLES/FEET
☐ WRISTS/HANDS   ☐ OTHER:

Session Details

WHAT STYLE DID YOU PRACTICE DURING THIS SESSION?

☐ ANUSARA   ☐ KRIPALU
☐ ASHTANGA   ☐ KUNDALINI
☐ BIKRAM   ☐ POWER
☐ IYENGAR   ☐ RESTORATIVE
☐ JIVAMUKTI   ☐ VINIYOGA
               ☐ OTHER:

WHAT TOOLS DID YOU HAVE ON HAND?

☐ MAT   ☐ STRAP
☐ WATER BOTTLE   ☐ BLANKET
☐ TOWEL   ☐ BOLSTER PILLOW
☐ BLOCK   ☐ OTHER:

SOUND ACCOMPANIMENT: ☐ NO MUSIC ☐ MUSIC

FAVORITE TRACK FROM TODAY'S SESSION
(TURN TO PAGE 26 AND ADD THE SONG TO YOUR YOGA SOUNDTRACK.)

Overall Session Rating

PACE OF FLOW: ① ② ③ ④ ⑤

DYNAMISM OF SEQUENCING: ① ② ③ ④ ⑤

DIFFICULTY: ① ② ③ ④ ⑤

POSES INCLUDED IN TODAY'S SEQUENCING:

☐ STANDING POSES   ☐ FORWARD BENDS
☐ BALANCING POSES   ☐ BACKBENDS
☐ SEATED POSES   ☐ INVERSIONS
☐ ABDOMINAL STRENGTHENERS ☐ RESTING POSES
☐ TWISTS

FAVORITE POSE OF TODAY'S SESSION:

MOST CHALLENGING POSE:

POSE YOU HADN'T TRIED BEFORE TODAY:

POSE IN WHICH YOU SHOWED THE MOST IMPROVEMENT:

POSE YOU'D LIKE TO WORK ON IN THE NEXT SESSION:

Dedication

Notes and Takeaways

Self-Review

One a scale of 1 to 5 (low to high), rate the following areas of your performance during this session:

FOCUS: ① ② ③ ④ ⑤

EVENNESS OF BREATH: ① ② ③ ④ ⑤

BALANCE: ① ② ③ ④ ⑤

STRENGTH: ① ② ③ ④ ⑤

ENERGY LEVEL: ① ② ③ ④ ⑤

ATTITUDE: ① ② ③ ④ ⑤

Yoga Session ③

DATE   /   /   TIME   START – FINISH

☐ **Group Class Practice**

NAME OF STUDIO: _____

NAME OF TEACHER: _____

TEACHER RATING (CIRCLE ONE): A+ A A- B C D F

CLASS LEVEL:
☐ BEGINNER ☐ INTERMEDIATE ☐ ADVANCED

CROWD LEVEL: ① ② ③ ④ ⑤
           NOT CROWDED ► CROWDED

TEMPERATURE: ☐ HEATED ☐ UNHEATED

(OR)

☐ **Home Practice and/or Private Instruction**

IN WHAT ROOM/SPACE DID YOU PRACTICE?

ON WHAT PART OF THE BODY DID YOU FOCUS DURING THIS SESSION?

☐ ABDOMINALS   ☐ HIPS
☐ BACK   ☐ BUTTOCKS
☐ SHOULDERS   ☐ LEGS
☐ ARMS   ☐ ANKLES/FEET
☐ WRISTS/HANDS ☐ OTHER:

Session Details

WHAT STYLE DID YOU PRACTICE DURING THIS SESSION?

☐ ANUSARA   ☐ KRIPALU
☐ ASHTANGA   ☐ KUNDALINI
☐ BIKRAM   ☐ POWER
☐ IYENGAR   ☐ RESTORATIVE
☐ JIVAMUKTI   ☐ VINIYOGA
                ☐ OTHER:

WHAT TOOLS DID YOU HAVE ON HAND?

☐ MAT   ☐ STRAP
☐ WATER BOTTLE ☐ BLANKET
☐ TOWEL   ☐ BOLSTER PILLOW
☐ BLOCK   ☐ OTHER:

SOUND ACCOMPANIMENT: ☐ NO MUSIC ☐ MUSIC

FAVORITE TRACK FROM TODAY'S SESSION
(TURN TO PAGE 20 AND ADD THE SONG TO YOUR YOGA SOUNDTRACK.)

Overall Session Rating

PACE OF FLOW: ① ② ③ ④ ⑤

DYNAMISM OF SEQUENCING: ① ② ③ ④ ⑤

DIFFICULTY: ① ② ③ ④ ⑤

POSES INCLUDED IN TODAY'S SEQUENCING:

☐ STANDING POSES   ☐ FORWARD BENDS
☐ BALANCING POSES   ☐ BACKBENDS
☐ SEATED POSES   ☐ INVERSIONS
☐ ABDOMINAL   ☐ RESTING POSES
   STRENGTHENERS
☐ TWISTS

FAVORITE POSE OF TODAY'S SESSION:

MOST CHALLENGING POSE:

POSE YOU HADN'T TRIED BEFORE TODAY:

POSE IN WHICH YOU SHOWED THE MOST IMPROVEMENT:

POSE YOU'D LIKE TO WORK ON IN THE NEXT SESSION:

Dedication

Notes and Takeaways

Self-Review

One a scale of 1 to 5 (low to high), rate the following areas of your performance during this session:

FOCUS: ① ② ③ ④ ⑤

EVENNESS OF BREATH: ① ② ③ ④ ⑤

BALANCE: ① ② ③ ④ ⑤

STRENGTH: ① ② ③ ④ ⑤

ENERGY LEVEL: ① ② ③ ④ ⑤

ATTITUDE: ① ② ③ ④ ⑤

DATE   /   /   TIME _____ - _____

☐ **Group Class Practice**   ☐ **Home Practice and/or Private Instruction**

NAME OF STUDIO: _____   (OR)   IN WHAT ROOM/SPACE DID YOU PRACTICE?

NAME OF TEACHER: _____

TEACHER RATING (CIRCLE ONE): A+ A A- B C D F   ON WHAT PART OF THE BODY DID YOU FOCUS DURING THIS SESSION?

CLASS LEVEL:
☐ BEGINNER   ☐ INTERMEDIATE   ☐ ADVANCED   ☐ ABDOMINALS   ☐ HIPS
                                                  ☐ BACK   ☐ BUTTOCKS
CROWD LEVEL: ① ② ③ ④ ⑤   ☐ SHOULDERS   ☐ LEGS
             NOT CROWDED ▸ CROWDED   ☐ ARMS   ☐ ANKLES/FEET
TEMPERATURE: ☐ HEATED   ☐ UNHEATED   ☐ WRISTS/HANDS ☐ OTHER:

Session Details

WHAT STYLE DID YOU PRACTICE DURING THIS SESSION?   WHAT TOOLS DID YOU HAVE ON HAND?

☐ ANUSARA   ☐ KRIPALU   ☐ MAT   ☐ STRAP
☐ ASHTANGA   ☐ KUNDALINI   ☐ WATER BOTTLE   ☐ BLANKET
☐ BIKRAM   ☐ POWER   ☐ TOWEL   ☐ BOLSTER PILLOW
☐ IYENGAR   ☐ RESTORATIVE   ☐ BLOCK   ☐ OTHER:
☐ JIVAMUKTI   ☐ VINIYOGA
                 ☐ OTHER:

SOUND ACCOMPANIMENT: ☐ NO MUSIC   ☐ MUSIC

FAVORITE TRACK FROM TODAY'S SESSION: _____
(TURN TO PAGE 20 AND ADD THE SONG TO YOUR YOGA SOUNDTRACK.)

Overall Session Rating

PACE OF FLOW: ① ② ③ ④ ⑤   FAVORITE POSE OF TODAY'S SESSION:

DYNAMISM OF SEQUENCING: ① ② ③ ④ ⑤
                                          MOST CHALLENGING POSE:
DIFFICULTY: ① ② ③ ④ ⑤

POSES INCLUDED IN TODAY'S SEQUENCING: POSE YOU HADN'T TRIED BEFORE TODAY:

☐ STANDING POSES   ☐ FORWARD BENDS
☐ BALANCING POSES   ☐ BACKBENDS
☐ SEATED POSES   ☐ INVERSIONS   POSE IN WHICH YOU SHOWED THE MOST IMPROVEMENT:
☐ ABDOMINAL   ☐ RESTING POSES
  STRENGTHENERS
☐ TWISTS   POSE YOU'D LIKE TO WORK ON IN THE NEXT SESSION:

Dedication

Notes and Takeaways

Self-Review

One a scale of 1 to 5 (low to high), rate the following areas of your performance during this session:

FOCUS: (1) (2) (3) (4) (5)

EVENNESS OF BREATH: (1) (2) (3) (4) (5)

BALANCE: (1) (2) (3) (4) (5)

STRENGTH: (1) (2) (3) (4) (5)

ENERGY LEVEL: (1) (2) (3) (4) (5)

ATTITUDE: (1) (2) (3) (4) (5)

DATE / / **TIME** START - FINISH

☐ **Group Class Practice**

NAME OF STUDIO: _____

NAME OF TEACHER: _____

TEACHER RATING (CIRCLE ONE): A+ A A- B C D F

CLASS LEVEL:
☐ BEGINNER ☐ INTERMEDIATE ☐ ADVANCED

CROWD LEVEL: (1)(2)(3)(4)(5)
NOT CROWDED ▸ CROWDED

TEMPERATURE: ☐ HEATED ☐ UNHEATED

(OR)

☐ **Home Practice and/or Private Instruction**

IN WHAT ROOM/SPACE DID YOU PRACTICE?

ON WHAT PART OF THE BODY DID YOU FOCUS DURING THIS SESSION?

☐ ABDOMINALS ☐ HIPS
☐ BACK ☐ BUTTOCKS
☐ SHOULDERS ☐ LEGS
☐ ARMS ☐ ANKLES/FEET
☐ WRISTS/HANDS ☐ OTHER: _____

Session Details

WHAT STYLE DID YOU PRACTICE DURING THIS SESSION?

☐ ANUSARA ☐ KRIPALU
☐ ASHTANGA ☐ KUNDALINI
☐ BIKRAM ☐ POWER
☐ IYENGAR ☐ RESTORATIVE
☐ JIVAMUKTI ☐ VINIYOGA
☐ OTHER: _____

WHAT TOOLS DID YOU HAVE ON HAND?

☐ MAT ☐ STRAP
☐ WATER BOTTLE ☐ BLANKET
☐ TOWEL ☐ BOLSTER PILLOW
☐ BLOCK ☐ OTHER: _____

SOUND ACCOMPANIMENT: ☐ NO MUSIC ☐ MUSIC

FAVORITE TRACK FROM TODAY'S SESSION
(TURN TO PAGE 20 AND ADD THE SONG TO YOUR YOGA SOUNDTRACK.)

Overall Session Rating

PACE OF FLOW: (1)(2)(3)(4)(5)

DYNAMISM OF SEQUENCING: (1)(2)(3)(4)(5)

DIFFICULTY: (1)(2)(3)(4)(5)

POSES INCLUDED IN TODAY'S SEQUENCING:

☐ STANDING POSES ☐ FORWARD BENDS
☐ BALANCING POSES ☐ BACKBENDS
☐ SEATED POSES ☐ INVERSIONS
☐ ABDOMINAL STRENGTHENERS ☐ RESTING POSES
☐ TWISTS

FAVORITE POSE OF TODAY'S SESSION:

MOST CHALLENGING POSE:

POSE YOU HADN'T TRIED BEFORE TODAY:

POSE IN WHICH YOU SHOWED THE MOST IMPROVEMENT:

POSE YOU'D LIKE TO WORK ON IN THE NEXT SESSION:

Dedication

TO WHOM OR WHAT DID YOU DEDICATE THIS CLASS?

Notes and Takeaways

Self-Review

One a scale of 1 to 5 (low to high), rate the following areas of your performance during this session:

FOCUS: 1 2 3 4 5

EVENNESS OF BREATH: 1 2 3 4 5

BALANCE: 1 2 3 4 5

STRENGTH: 1 2 3 4 5

ENERGY LEVEL: 1 2 3 4 5

ATTITUDE: 1 2 3 4 5

DATE / / **TIME** START - FINISH

☐ Group Class Practice

NAME OF STUDIO: _____

NAME OF TEACHER: _____

TEACHER RATING (CIRCLE ONE): A+ A A- B C D F

CLASS LEVEL:
☐ BEGINNER ☐ INTERMEDIATE ☐ ADVANCED

CROWD LEVEL: ① ② ③ ④ ⑤
NOT CROWDED ▸ CROWDED

TEMPERATURE: ☐ HEATED ☐ UNHEATED

(OR)

☐ Home Practice and/or Private Instruction

IN WHAT ROOM/SPACE DID YOU PRACTICE?
_____

ON WHAT PART OF THE BODY DID YOU FOCUS DURING THIS SESSION?

☐ ABDOMINALS   ☐ HIPS
☐ BACK   ☐ BUTTOCKS
☐ SHOULDERS   ☐ LEGS
☐ ARMS   ☐ ANKLES/FEET
☐ WRISTS/HANDS   ☐ OTHER: _____

Session Details

WHAT STYLE DID YOU PRACTICE DURING THIS SESSION?

☐ ANUSARA   ☐ KRIPALU
☐ ASHTANGA   ☐ KUNDALINI
☐ BIKRAM   ☐ POWER
☐ IYENGAR   ☐ RESTORATIVE
☐ JIVAMUKTI   ☐ VINIYOGA
   ☐ OTHER: _____

WHAT TOOLS DID YOU HAVE ON HAND?

☐ MAT   ☐ STRAP
☐ WATER BOTTLE   ☐ BLANKET
☐ TOWEL   ☐ BOLSTER PILLOW
☐ BLOCK   ☐ OTHER: _____

SOUND ACCOMPANIMENT: ☐ NO MUSIC ☐ MUSIC

FAVORITE TRACK FROM TODAY'S SESSION
(TURN TO PAGE 20 AND ADD THE SONG TO YOUR YOGA SOUNDTRACK.)

Overall Session Rating

PACE OF FLOW: ① ② ③ ④ ⑤

DYNAMISM OF SEQUENCING: ① ② ③ ④ ⑤

DIFFICULTY: ① ② ③ ④ ⑤

POSES INCLUDED IN TODAY'S SEQUENCING:

☐ STANDING POSES   ☐ FORWARD BENDS
☐ BALANCING POSES   ☐ BACKBENDS
☐ SEATED POSES   ☐ INVERSIONS
☐ ABDOMINAL STRENGTHENERS   ☐ RESTING POSES
☐ TWISTS

FAVORITE POSE OF TODAY'S SESSION:

MOST CHALLENGING POSE:

POSE YOU HADN'T TRIED BEFORE TODAY:

POSE IN WHICH YOU SHOWED THE MOST IMPROVEMENT:

POSE YOU'D LIKE TO WORK ON IN THE NEXT SESSION:

Dedication

Notes and Takeaways

Self-Review

One a scale of 1 to 5 (low to high), rate the following areas of your performance during this session:

FOCUS: 1 2 3 4 5

EVENNESS OF BREATH: 1 2 3 4 5

BALANCE: 1 2 3 4 5

STRENGTH: 1 2 3 4 5

ENERGY LEVEL: 1 2 3 4 5

ATTITUDE: 1 2 3 4 5

DATE   /   /   TIME   START - FINISH

☐ **Group Class Practice**   ☐ **Home Practice and/or Private Instruction**

NAME OF STUDIO: _____   (OR)   IN WHAT ROOM/SPACE DID YOU PRACTICE?

NAME OF TEACHER: _____

TEACHER RATING (CIRCLE ONE): A+ A A- B C D F   ON WHAT PART OF THE BODY DID YOU FOCUS DURING THIS SESSION?

CLASS LEVEL:
☐ BEGINNER ☐ INTERMEDIATE ☐ ADVANCED

CROWD LEVEL: ①②③④⑤
NOT CROWDED → CROWDED

TEMPERATURE: ☐ HEATED ☐ UNHEATED

☐ ABDOMINALS ☐ HIPS
☐ BACK ☐ BUTTOCKS
☐ SHOULDERS ☐ LEGS
☐ ARMS ☐ ANKLES/FEET
☐ WRISTS/HANDS ☐ OTHER:

Session Details

WHAT STYLE DID YOU PRACTICE DURING THIS SESSION?
☐ ANUSARA ☐ KRIPALU
☐ ASHTANGA ☐ KUNDALINI
☐ BIKRAM ☐ POWER
☐ IYENGAR ☐ RESTORATIVE
☐ JIVAMUKTI ☐ VINIYOGA
☐ OTHER:

WHAT TOOLS DID YOU HAVE ON HAND?
☐ MAT ☐ STRAP
☐ WATER BOTTLE ☐ BLANKET
☐ TOWEL ☐ BOLSTER PILLOW
☐ BLOCK ☐ OTHER:

SOUND ACCOMPANIMENT: ☐ NO MUSIC ☐ MUSIC

FAVORITE TRACK FROM TODAY'S SESSION
(TURN TO PAGE 20 AND ADD THE SONG TO YOUR YOGA SOUNDTRACK.)

Overall Session Rating

PACE OF FLOW: ①②③④⑤

DYNAMISM OF SEQUENCING: ①②③④⑤

DIFFICULTY: ①②③④⑤

POSES INCLUDED IN TODAY'S SEQUENCING:
☐ STANDING POSES ☐ FORWARD BENDS
☐ BALANCING POSES ☐ BACKBENDS
☐ SEATED POSES ☐ INVERSIONS
☐ ABDOMINAL STRENGTHENERS ☐ RESTING POSES
☐ TWISTS

FAVORITE POSE OF TODAY'S SESSION:

MOST CHALLENGING POSE:

POSE YOU HADN'T TRIED BEFORE TODAY:

POSE IN WHICH YOU SHOWED THE MOST IMPROVEMENT:

POSE YOU'D LIKE TO WORK ON IN THE NEXT SESSION:

Dedication

TO WHOM OR WHAT DID YOU DEDICATE THIS CLASS?

Notes and Takeaways

Self-Review

One a scale of 1 to 5 (low to high), rate the following areas of your performance during this session:

FOCUS: ① ② ③ ④ ⑤

EVENNESS OF BREATH: ① ② ③ ④ ⑤

BALANCE: ① ② ③ ④ ⑤

STRENGTH: ① ② ③ ④ ⑤

ENERGY LEVEL: ① ② ③ ④ ⑤

ATTITUDE: ① ② ③ ④ ⑤

DATE / /   TIME

☐ **Group Class Practice**

☐ **Home Practice and/or Private Instruction**

NAME OF STUDIO: _____ (OR) IN WHAT ROOM/SPACE DID YOU PRACTICE?

NAME OF TEACHER: _____

TEACHER RATING (CIRCLE ONE): A+ A A- B C D F

CLASS LEVEL:
☐ BEGINNER ☐ INTERMEDIATE ☐ ADVANCED

CROWD LEVEL: ① ② ③ ④ ⑤
        NOT CROWDED ▸ CROWDED

TEMPERATURE: ☐ HEATED ☐ UNHEATED

ON WHAT PART OF THE BODY DID YOU FOCUS DURING THIS SESSION?
☐ ABDOMINALS ☐ HIPS
☐ BACK ☐ BUTTOCKS
☐ SHOULDERS ☐ LEGS
☐ ARMS ☐ ANKLES/FEET
☐ WRISTS/HANDS ☐ OTHER: _____

Session Details

WHAT STYLE DID YOU PRACTICE DURING THIS SESSION?
☐ ANUSARA ☐ KRIPALU
☐ ASHTANGA ☐ KUNDALINI
☐ BIKRAM ☐ POWER
☐ IYENGAR ☐ RESTORATIVE
☐ JIVAMUKTI ☐ VINIYOGA
☐ OTHER: _____

WHAT TOOLS DID YOU HAVE ON HAND?
☐ MAT ☐ STRAP
☐ WATER BOTTLE ☐ BLANKET
☐ TOWEL ☐ BOLSTER PILLOW
☐ BLOCK ☐ OTHER: _____

SOUND ACCOMPANIMENT: ☐ NO MUSIC ☐ MUSIC

FAVORITE TRACK FROM TODAY'S SESSION
(TURN TO PAGE 20 AND ADD THE SONG TO YOUR YOGA SOUNDTRACK.)

Overall Session Rating

PACE OF FLOW: ① ② ③ ④ ⑤

DYNAMISM OF SEQUENCING: ① ② ③ ④ ⑤

DIFFICULTY: ① ② ③ ④ ⑤

POSES INCLUDED IN TODAY'S SEQUENCING:
☐ STANDING POSES ☐ FORWARD BENDS
☐ BALANCING POSES ☐ BACKBENDS
☐ SEATED POSES ☐ INVERSIONS
☐ ABDOMINAL STRENGTHENERS ☐ RESTING POSES
☐ TWISTS

FAVORITE POSE OF TODAY'S SESSION:

MOST CHALLENGING POSE:

POSE YOU HADN'T TRIED BEFORE TODAY:

POSE IN WHICH YOU SHOWED THE MOST IMPROVEMENT:

POSE YOU'D LIKE TO WORK ON IN THE NEXT SESSION:

Dedication

Notes and Takeaways

Self-Review

One a scale of 1 to 5 (low to high), rate the following areas of your performance during this session:

FOCUS: 1 2 3 4 5

EVENNESS OF BREATH: 1 2 3 4 5

BALANCE: 1 2 3 4 5

STRENGTH: 1 2 3 4 5

ENERGY LEVEL: 1 2 3 4 5

ATTITUDE: 1 2 3 4 5

DATE   /   /   TIME START - FINISH

☐ **Group Class Practice**

☐ **Home Practice and/or Private Instruction**

NAME OF STUDIO: _____   (OR)   IN WHAT ROOM/SPACE DID YOU PRACTICE?

NAME OF TEACHER: _____

TEACHER RATING (CIRCLE ONE): A+ A A- B C D F

CLASS LEVEL:

☐ BEGINNER ☐ INTERMEDIATE ☐ ADVANCED

CROWD LEVEL: (1)(2)(3)(4)(5)
             NOT CROWDED ▸ CROWDED

TEMPERATURE: ☐ HEATED ☐ UNHEATED

ON WHAT PART OF THE BODY DID YOU FOCUS DURING THIS SESSION?

☐ ABDOMINALS ☐ HIPS
☐ BACK ☐ BUTTOCKS
☐ SHOULDERS ☐ LEGS
☐ ARMS ☐ ANKLES/FEET
☐ WRISTS/HANDS ☐ OTHER: _____

Session Details

WHAT STYLE DID YOU PRACTICE DURING THIS SESSION?

☐ ANUSARA ☐ KRIPALU
☐ ASHTANGA ☐ KUNDALINI
☐ BIKRAM ☐ POWER
☐ IYENGAR ☐ RESTORATIVE
☐ JIVAMUKTI ☐ VINIYOGA
          ☐ OTHER: _____

WHAT TOOLS DID YOU HAVE ON HAND?

☐ MAT ☐ STRAP
☐ WATER BOTTLE ☐ BLANKET
☐ TOWEL ☐ BOLSTER PILLOW
☐ BLOCK ☐ OTHER: _____

SOUND ACCOMPANIMENT: ☐ NO MUSIC ☐ MUSIC

FAVORITE TRACK FROM TODAY'S SESSION
(TURN TO PAGE 20 AND ADD THE SONG TO YOUR YOGA SOUNDTRACK.)

Overall Session Rating

PACE OF FLOW: (1)(2)(3)(4)(5)

DYNAMISM OF SEQUENCING: (1)(2)(3)(4)(5)

DIFFICULTY: (1)(2)(3)(4)(5)

POSES INCLUDED IN TODAY'S SEQUENCING:

☐ STANDING POSES ☐ FORWARD BENDS
☐ BALANCING POSES ☐ BACKBENDS
☐ SEATED POSES ☐ INVERSIONS
☐ ABDOMINAL STRENGTHENERS ☐ RESTING POSES
☐ TWISTS

FAVORITE POSE OF TODAY'S SESSION:

MOST CHALLENGING POSE:

POSE YOU HADN'T TRIED BEFORE TODAY:

POSE IN WHICH YOU SHOWED THE MOST IMPROVEMENT:

POSE YOU'D LIKE TO WORK ON IN THE NEXT SESSION:

Dedication

Notes and Takeaways

Self-Review

One a scale of 1 to 5 (low to high), rate the following areas of your performance during this session:

FOCUS: ① ② ③ ④ ⑤

EVENNESS OF BREATH: ① ② ③ ④ ⑤

BALANCE: ① ② ③ ④ ⑤

STRENGTH: ① ② ③ ④ ⑤

ENERGY LEVEL: ① ② ③ ④ ⑤

ATTITUDE: ① ② ③ ④ ⑤

DATE   /   /   TIME

☐ **Group Class Practice**   ☐ **Home Practice and/or Private Instruction**

NAME OF STUDIO: _____   (OR)   IN WHAT ROOM/SPACE DID YOU PRACTICE?

NAME OF TEACHER: _____

TEACHER RATING (CIRCLE ONE): A+ A A- B C D F

CLASS LEVEL: ON WHAT PART OF THE BODY DID YOU FOCUS DURING THIS SESSION?
☐ BEGINNER ☐ INTERMEDIATE ☐ ADVANCED
                                               ☐ ABDOMINALS   ☐ HIPS
                                               ☐ BACK   ☐ BUTTOCKS
CROWD LEVEL: (1)(2)(3)(4)(5)   ☐ SHOULDERS   ☐ LEGS
         NOT CROWDED ▸ CROWDED   ☐ ARMS   ☐ ANKLES/FEET
TEMPERATURE: ☐ HEATED ☐ UNHEATED   ☐ WRISTS/HANDS   ☐ OTHER:

Session Details

WHAT STYLE DID YOU PRACTICE DURING THIS SESSION?   WHAT TOOLS DID YOU HAVE ON HAND?
☐ ANUSARA   ☐ KRIPALU   ☐ MAT   ☐ STRAP
☐ ASHTANGA   ☐ KUNDALINI   ☐ WATER BOTTLE   ☐ BLANKET
☐ BIKRAM   ☐ POWER   ☐ TOWEL   ☐ BOLSTER PILLOW
☐ IYENGAR   ☐ RESTORATIVE   ☐ BLOCK   ☐ OTHER:
☐ JIVAMUKTI   ☐ VINIYOGA
                 ☐ OTHER:

SOUND ACCOMPANIMENT: ☐ NO MUSIC   ☐ MUSIC

FAVORITE TRACK FROM TODAY'S SESSION
(TURN TO PAGE 20 AND ADD THE SONG TO YOUR YOGA SOUNDTRACK.)

Overall Session Rating

PACE OF FLOW: (1)(2)(3)(4)(5)   FAVORITE POSE OF TODAY'S SESSION:

DYNAMISM OF
SEQUENCING: (1)(2)(3)(4)(5)   MOST CHALLENGING POSE:

DIFFICULTY: (1)(2)(3)(4)(5)

POSES INCLUDED IN TODAY'S SEQUENCING: POSE YOU HADN'T TRIED BEFORE TODAY:

☐ STANDING POSES   ☐ FORWARD BENDS
☐ BALANCING POSES ☐ BACKBENDS   POSE IN WHICH YOU SHOWED THE MOST IMPROVEMENT:
☐ SEATED POSES   ☐ INVERSIONS
☐ ABDOMINAL   ☐ RESTING POSES
  STRENGTHENERS   POSE YOU'D LIKE TO WORK ON IN THE NEXT SESSION:
☐ TWISTS

Dedication

Notes and Takeaways

Self-Review

One a scale of 1 to 5 (low to high), rate the following areas of your performance during this session:

FOCUS: ① ② ③ ④ ⑤

EVENNESS OF BREATH: ① ② ③ ④ ⑤

BALANCE: ① ② ③ ④ ⑤

STRENGTH: ① ② ③ ④ ⑤

ENERGY LEVEL: ① ② ③ ④ ⑤

ATTITUDE: ① ② ③ ④ ⑤

Yoga Session 11

DATE   /   /   TIME START - FINISH

☐ **Group Class Practice**   ☐ **Home Practice and/or**
                                                  Private Instruction

NAME OF STUDIO: (OR)   IN WHAT ROOM/SPACE DID YOU PRACTICE?

NAME OF TEACHER:

TEACHER RATING (CIRCLE ONE): A+ A A- B C D F   ON WHAT PART OF THE BODY DID YOU FOCUS
                                                 DURING THIS SESSION?
CLASS LEVEL:
☐ BEGINNER ☐ INTERMEDIATE ☐ ADVANCED   ☐ ABDOMINALS   ☐ HIPS
                                           ☐ BACK   ☐ BUTTOCKS
CROWD LEVEL: ①②③④⑤   ☐ SHOULDERS   ☐ LEGS
          NOT CROWDED ▸ CROWDED   ☐ ARMS   ☐ ANKLES/FEET
TEMPERATURE: ☐ HEATED   ☐ UNHEATED   ☐ WRISTS/HANDS   ☐ OTHER:

Session Details

WHAT STYLE DID YOU PRACTICE DURING THIS SESSION?   WHAT TOOLS DID YOU HAVE ON HAND?
☐ ANUSARA   ☐ KRIPALU   ☐ MAT   ☐ STRAP
☐ ASHTANGA   ☐ KUNDALINI   ☐ WATER BOTTLE   ☐ BLANKET
☐ BIKRAM   ☐ POWER   ☐ TOWEL   ☐ BOLSTER PILLOW
☐ IYENGAR   ☐ RESTORATIVE   ☐ BLOCK   ☐ OTHER:
☐ JIVAMUKTI   ☐ VINIYOGA
                 ☐ OTHER:

SOUND ACCOMPANIMENT: ☐ NO MUSIC   ☐ MUSIC

FAVORITE TRACK FROM TODAY'S SESSION
(TURN TO PAGE 20 AND ADD THE SONG TO YOUR YOGA SOUNDTRACK.)

Overall Session Rating

PACE OF FLOW: ①②③④⑤   FAVORITE POSE OF TODAY'S SESSION:

DYNAMISM OF
SEQUENCING: ①②③④⑤

DIFFICULTY: ①②③④⑤   MOST CHALLENGING POSE:

POSES INCLUDED IN TODAY'S SEQUENCING: POSE YOU HADN'T TRIED BEFORE TODAY:

☐ STANDING POSES   ☐ FORWARD BENDS
☐ BALANCING POSES   ☐ BACKBENDS
☐ SEATED POSES   ☐ INVERSIONS   POSE IN WHICH YOU SHOWED THE MOST IMPROVEMENT:
☐ ABDOMINAL   ☐ RESTING POSES
  STRENGTHENERS
☐ TWISTS   POSE YOU'D LIKE TO WORK ON IN THE NEXT SESSION:

Dedication

Notes and Takeaways

Self-Review

One a scale of 1 to 5 (low to high), rate the following areas of your performance during this session:

FOCUS: (1)(2)(3)(4)(5)

EVENNESS OF BREATH: (1)(2)(3)(4)(5)

BALANCE: (1)(2)(3)(4)(5)

STRENGTH: (1)(2)(3)(4)(5)

ENERGY LEVEL: (1)(2)(3)(4)(5)

ATTITUDE: (1)(2)(3)(4)(5)

DATE   /   /   TIME   -

☐ **Group Class Practice**   ☐ **Home Practice and/or Private Instruction**

NAME OF STUDIO: _____   (OR)   IN WHAT ROOM/SPACE DID YOU PRACTICE?

NAME OF TEACHER: _____

TEACHER RATING (CIRCLE ONE): A+ A A- B C D F

CLASS LEVEL: ON WHAT PART OF THE BODY DID YOU FOCUS DURING THIS SESSION?
☐ BEGINNER ☐ INTERMEDIATE ☐ ADVANCED   ☐ ABDOMINALS   ☐ HIPS
                                              ☐ BACK   ☐ BUTTOCKS
CROWD LEVEL: ①②③④⑤   ☐ SHOULDERS   ☐ LEGS
           NOT CROWDED ► CROWDED   ☐ ARMS   ☐ ANKLES/FEET
TEMPERATURE: ☐ HEATED   ☐ UNHEATED   ☐ WRISTS/HANDS   ☐ OTHER: _____

Session Details

WHAT STYLE DID YOU PRACTICE DURING THIS SESSION?   WHAT TOOLS DID YOU HAVE ON HAND?
☐ ANUSARA   ☐ KRIPALU   ☐ MAT   ☐ STRAP
☐ ASHTANGA   ☐ KUNDALINI   ☐ WATER BOTTLE   ☐ BLANKET
☐ BIKRAM   ☐ POWER   ☐ TOWEL   ☐ BOLSTER PILLOW
☐ IYENGAR   ☐ RESTORATIVE   ☐ BLOCK   ☐ OTHER: _____
☐ JIVAMUKTI   ☐ VINIYOGA
               ☐ OTHER: _____

SOUND ACCOMPANIMENT: ☐ NO MUSIC   ☐ MUSIC

FAVORITE TRACK FROM TODAY'S SESSION
(TURN TO PAGE 20 AND ADD THE SONG TO YOUR YOGA SOUNDTRACK.)

Overall Session Rating

PACE OF FLOW: ①②③④⑤   FAVORITE POSE OF TODAY'S SESSION:

DYNAMISM OF SEQUENCING: ①②③④⑤

DIFFICULTY: ①②③④⑤   MOST CHALLENGING POSE:

POSES INCLUDED IN TODAY'S SEQUENCING: POSE YOU HADN'T TRIED BEFORE TODAY:

☐ STANDING POSES   ☐ FORWARD BENDS
☐ BALANCING POSES   ☐ BACKBENDS   POSE IN WHICH YOU SHOWED THE MOST IMPROVEMENT:
☐ SEATED POSES   ☐ INVERSIONS
☐ ABDOMINAL   ☐ RESTING POSES
   STRENGTHENERS   POSE YOU'D LIKE TO WORK ON IN THE NEXT SESSION:
☐ TWISTS

Dedication

TO WHOM OR WHAT DID YOU DEDICATE THIS CLASS?

Notes and Takeaways

Self-Review

One a scale of 1 to 5 (low to high), rate the following areas of your performance during this session:

FOCUS: ① ② ③ ④ ⑤

EVENNESS OF BREATH: ① ② ③ ④ ⑤

BALANCE: ① ② ③ ④ ⑤

STRENGTH: ① ② ③ ④ ⑤

ENERGY LEVEL: ① ② ③ ④ ⑤

ATTITUDE: ① ② ③ ④ ⑤

DATE / / **TIME** START - FINISH

☐ **Group Class Practice**

NAME OF STUDIO:

NAME OF TEACHER:

TEACHER RATING (CIRCLE ONE): A+ A A- B C D F

CLASS LEVEL:
☐ BEGINNER ☐ INTERMEDIATE ☐ ADVANCED

CROWD LEVEL: ① ② ③ ④ ⑤
NOT CROWDED ▸ CROWDED

TEMPERATURE: ☐ HEATED ☐ UNHEATED

(OR)

☐ **Home Practice and/or Private Instruction**

IN WHAT ROOM/SPACE DID YOU PRACTICE?

ON WHAT PART OF THE BODY DID YOU FOCUS DURING THIS SESSION?

☐ ABDOMINALS ☐ HIPS
☐ BACK ☐ BUTTOCKS
☐ SHOULDERS ☐ LEGS
☐ ARMS ☐ ANKLES/FEET
☐ WRISTS/HANDS ☐ OTHER:

Session Details

WHAT STYLE DID YOU PRACTICE DURING THIS SESSION?
☐ ANUSARA ☐ KRIPALU
☐ ASHTANGA ☐ KUNDALINI
☐ BIKRAM ☐ POWER
☐ IYENGAR ☐ RESTORATIVE
☐ JIVAMUKTI ☐ VINIYOGA
☐ OTHER:

WHAT TOOLS DID YOU HAVE ON HAND?
☐ MAT ☐ STRAP
☐ WATER BOTTLE ☐ BLANKET
☐ TOWEL ☐ BOLSTER PILLOW
☐ BLOCK ☐ OTHER:

SOUND ACCOMPANIMENT: ☐ NO MUSIC ☐ MUSIC

FAVORITE TRACK FROM TODAY'S SESSION
(TURN TO PAGE 20 AND ADD THE SONG TO YOUR YOGA SOUNDTRACK.)

Overall Session Rating

PACE OF FLOW: ① ② ③ ④ ⑤

DYNAMISM OF SEQUENCING: ① ② ③ ④ ⑤

DIFFICULTY: ① ② ③ ④ ⑤

POSES INCLUDED IN TODAY'S SEQUENCING:
☐ STANDING POSES ☐ FORWARD BENDS
☐ BALANCING POSES ☐ BACKBENDS
☐ SEATED POSES ☐ INVERSIONS
☐ ABDOMINAL STRENGTHENERS ☐ RESTING POSES
☐ TWISTS

FAVORITE POSE OF TODAY'S SESSION:

MOST CHALLENGING POSE:

POSE YOU HADN'T TRIED BEFORE TODAY:

POSE IN WHICH YOU SHOWED THE MOST IMPROVEMENT:

POSE YOU'D LIKE TO WORK ON IN THE NEXT SESSION:

Dedication

Notes and Takeaways

Self-Review

One a scale of 1 to 5 (low to high), rate the following areas of your performance during this session:

FOCUS: 1 2 3 4 5

EVENNESS OF BREATH: 1 2 3 4 5

BALANCE: 1 2 3 4 5

STRENGTH: 1 2 3 4 5

ENERGY LEVEL: 1 2 3 4 5

ATTITUDE: 1 2 3 4 5

DATE   /   /   TIME   -

☐ **Group Class Practice**   ☐ **Home Practice and/or Private Instruction**

NAME OF STUDIO: _____   (OR)   IN WHAT ROOM/SPACE DID YOU PRACTICE?

NAME OF TEACHER: _____

TEACHER RATING (CIRCLE ONE): A+ A A- B C D F

CLASS LEVEL:

☐ BEGINNER ☐ INTERMEDIATE ☐ ADVANCED

CROWD LEVEL: (1)(2)(3)(4)(5)

NOT CROWDED ▸ CROWDED

TEMPERATURE: ☐ HEATED ☐ UNHEATED

ON WHAT PART OF THE BODY DID YOU FOCUS DURING THIS SESSION?

☐ ABDOMINALS   ☐ HIPS
☐ BACK   ☐ BUTTOCKS
☐ SHOULDERS   ☐ LEGS
☐ ARMS   ☐ ANKLES/FEET
☐ WRISTS/HANDS ☐ OTHER:

Session Details

WHAT STYLE DID YOU PRACTICE DURING THIS SESSION?

☐ ANUSARA   ☐ KRIPALU
☐ ASHTANGA   ☐ KUNDALINI
☐ BIKRAM   ☐ POWER
☐ IYENGAR   ☐ RESTORATIVE
☐ JIVAMUKTI   ☐ VINIYOGA
               ☐ OTHER: _____

WHAT TOOLS DID YOU HAVE ON HAND?

☐ MAT   ☐ STRAP
☐ WATER BOTTLE ☐ BLANKET
☐ TOWEL   ☐ BOLSTER PILLOW
☐ BLOCK   ☐ OTHER:

SOUND ACCOMPANIMENT: ☐ NO MUSIC ☐ MUSIC

FAVORITE TRACK FROM TODAY'S SESSION
(TURN TO PAGE 20 AND ADD THE SONG TO YOUR YOGA SOUNDTRACK.)

Overall Session Rating

PACE OF FLOW: (1)(2)(3)(4)(5)

DYNAMISM OF SEQUENCING: (1)(2)(3)(4)(5)

DIFFICULTY: (1)(2)(3)(4)(5)

POSES INCLUDED IN TODAY'S SEQUENCING:

☐ STANDING POSES   ☐ FORWARD BENDS
☐ BALANCING POSES   ☐ BACKBENDS
☐ SEATED POSES   ☐ INVERSIONS
☐ ABDOMINAL STRENGTHENERS ☐ RESTING POSES
☐ TWISTS

FAVORITE POSE OF TODAY'S SESSION:

MOST CHALLENGING POSE:

POSE YOU HADN'T TRIED BEFORE TODAY:

POSE IN WHICH YOU SHOWED THE MOST IMPROVEMENT:

POSE YOU'D LIKE TO WORK ON IN THE NEXT SESSION:

Dedication

Notes and Takeaways

Self-Review

One a scale of 1 to 5 (low to high), rate the following areas of your performance during this session:

FOCUS: 1 2 3 4 5

EVENNESS
OF BREATH: 1 2 3 4 5

BALANCE: 1 2 3 4 5

STRENGTH: 1 2 3 4 5

ENERGY
LEVEL: 1 2 3 4 5

ATTITUDE: 1 2 3 4 5

Yoga Session 15

DATE   /   /   TIME START - FINISH

☐ **Group Class Practice**

☐ **Home Practice and/or Private Instruction**

NAME OF STUDIO: _____   (OR)   IN WHAT ROOM/SPACE DID YOU PRACTICE?

NAME OF TEACHER: _____

TEACHER RATING (CIRCLE ONE): A+ A A- B C D F

CLASS LEVEL:

☐ BEGINNER   ☐ INTERMEDIATE   ☐ ADVANCED

CROWD LEVEL: ① ② ③ ④ ⑤
              NOT CROWDED ▶ CROWDED

TEMPERATURE: ☐ HEATED   ☐ UNHEATED

ON WHAT PART OF THE BODY DID YOU FOCUS DURING THIS SESSION?

☐ ABDOMINALS   ☐ HIPS
☐ BACK   ☐ BUTTOCKS
☐ SHOULDERS   ☐ LEGS
☐ ARMS   ☐ ANKLES/FEET
☐ WRISTS/HANDS ☐ OTHER:

Session Details

WHAT STYLE DID YOU PRACTICE DURING THIS SESSION?

☐ ANUSARA   ☐ KRIPALU
☐ ASHTANGA   ☐ KUNDALINI
☐ BIKRAM   ☐ POWER
☐ IYENGAR   ☐ RESTORATIVE
☐ JIVAMUKTI   ☐ VINIYOGA
                ☐ OTHER:

WHAT TOOLS DID YOU HAVE ON HAND?

☐ MAT   ☐ STRAP
☐ WATER BOTTLE ☐ BLANKET
☐ TOWEL   ☐ BOLSTER PILLOW
☐ BLOCK ·   ☐ OTHER:

SOUND ACCOMPANIMENT: ☐ NO MUSIC   ☐ MUSIC

FAVORITE TRACK FROM TODAY'S SESSION
(TURN TO PAGE 20 AND ADD THE SONG TO YOUR YOGA SOUNDTRACK.)

Overall Session Rating

PACE OF FLOW: ① ② ③ ④ ⑤

DYNAMISM OF SEQUENCING: ① ② ③ ④ ⑤

DIFFICULTY: ① ② ③ ④ ⑤

POSES INCLUDED IN TODAY'S SEQUENCING:

☐ STANDING POSES   ☐ FORWARD BENDS
☐ BALANCING POSES   ☐ BACKBENDS
☐ SEATED POSES   ☐ INVERSIONS
☐ ABDOMINAL   ☐ RESTING POSES
  STRENGTHENERS
☐ TWISTS

FAVORITE POSE OF TODAY'S SESSION:

MOST CHALLENGING POSE:

POSE YOU HADN'T TRIED BEFORE TODAY:

POSE IN WHICH YOU SHOWED THE MOST IMPROVEMENT:

POSE YOU'D LIKE TO WORK ON IN THE NEXT SESSION:

Dedication

Notes and Takeaways

Self-Review

One a scale of 1 to 5 (low to high), rate the following areas of your performance during this session:

FOCUS: ① ② ③ ④ ⑤

EVENNESS OF BREATH: ① ② ③ ④ ⑤

BALANCE: ① ② ③ ④ ⑤

STRENGTH: ① ② ③ ④ ⑤

ENERGY LEVEL: ① ② ③ ④ ⑤

ATTITUDE: ① ② ③ ④ ⑤

Yoga Session (16)

DATE / /   **TIME** START – FINISH

☐ **Group Class Practice**

☐ **Home Practice and/or Private Instruction**

NAME OF STUDIO: _____ (OR)   IN WHAT ROOM/SPACE DID YOU PRACTICE?

NAME OF TEACHER: _____

TEACHER RATING (CIRCLE ONE): A+ A A- B C D F

CLASS LEVEL:
☐ BEGINNER ☐ INTERMEDIATE ☐ ADVANCED

CROWD LEVEL: ①–②–③–④–⑤
     NOT CROWDED → CROWDED

TEMPERATURE: ☐ HEATED ☐ UNHEATED

ON WHAT PART OF THE BODY DID YOU FOCUS DURING THIS SESSION?
☐ ABDOMINALS ☐ HIPS
☐ BACK ☐ BUTTOCKS
☐ SHOULDERS ☐ LEGS
☐ ARMS ☐ ANKLES/FEET
☐ WRISTS/HANDS ☐ OTHER: _____

Session Details

WHAT STYLE DID YOU PRACTICE DURING THIS SESSION?
☐ ANUSARA ☐ KRIPALU
☐ ASHTANGA ☐ KUNDALINI
☐ BIKRAM ☐ POWER
☐ IYENGAR ☐ RESTORATIVE
☐ JIVAMUKTI ☐ VINIYOGA
     ☐ OTHER: _____

WHAT TOOLS DID YOU HAVE ON HAND?
☐ MAT ☐ STRAP
☐ WATER BOTTLE ☐ BLANKET
☐ TOWEL ☐ BOLSTER PILLOW
☐ BLOCK ☐ OTHER: _____

SOUND ACCOMPANIMENT: ☐ NO MUSIC ☐ MUSIC

FAVORITE TRACK FROM TODAY'S SESSION
(TURN TO PAGE 20 AND ADD THE SONG TO YOUR YOGA SOUNDTRACK.)

Overall Session Rating

PACE OF FLOW: ①②③④⑤

DYNAMISM OF SEQUENCING: ①②③④⑤

DIFFICULTY: ①②③④⑤

POSES INCLUDED IN TODAY'S SEQUENCING:
☐ STANDING POSES ☐ FORWARD BENDS
☐ BALANCING POSES ☐ BACKBENDS
☐ SEATED POSES ☐ INVERSIONS
☐ ABDOMINAL STRENGTHENERS ☐ RESTING POSES
☐ TWISTS

FAVORITE POSE OF TODAY'S SESSION:

MOST CHALLENGING POSE:

POSE YOU HADN'T TRIED BEFORE TODAY:

POSE IN WHICH YOU SHOWED THE MOST IMPROVEMENT:

POSE YOU'D LIKE TO WORK ON IN THE NEXT SESSION:

Dedication

TO WHOM OR WHAT DID YOU DEDICATE THIS CLASS?

Notes and Takeaways

Self-Review

One a scale of 1 to 5 (low to high), rate the following areas of your performance during this session:

FOCUS: ① ② ③ ④ ⑤

EVENNESS OF BREATH: ① ② ③ ④ ⑤

BALANCE: ① ② ③ ④ ⑤

STRENGTH: ① ② ③ ④ ⑤

ENERGY LEVEL: ① ② ③ ④ ⑤

ATTITUDE: ① ② ③ ④ ⑤

DATE   /   /   TIME START - FINISH

☐ **Group Class Practice**

☐ **Home Practice and/or Private Instruction**

OR

NAME OF STUDIO: _____

IN WHAT ROOM/SPACE DID YOU PRACTICE?

NAME OF TEACHER: _____

TEACHER RATING (CIRCLE ONE): A+ A A- B C D F

ON WHAT PART OF THE BODY DID YOU FOCUS DURING THIS SESSION?

CLASS LEVEL:
☐ BEGINNER ☐ INTERMEDIATE ☐ ADVANCED

☐ ABDOMINALS   ☐ HIPS
☐ BACK   ☐ BUTTOCKS

CROWD LEVEL: ①②③④⑤
NOT CROWDED ► CROWDED

☐ SHOULDERS   ☐ LEGS
☐ ARMS   ☐ ANKLES/FEET

TEMPERATURE: ☐ HEATED   ☐ UNHEATED

☐ WRISTS/HANDS ☐ OTHER:

Session Details

WHAT STYLE DID YOU PRACTICE DURING THIS SESSION?

☐ ANUSARA   ☐ KRIPALU
☐ ASHTANGA   ☐ KUNDALINI
☐ BIKRAM   ☐ POWER
☐ IYENGAR   ☐ RESTORATIVE
☐ JIVAMUKTI   ☐ VINIYOGA
               ☐ OTHER: _____

WHAT TOOLS DID YOU HAVE ON HAND?

☐ MAT   ☐ STRAP
☐ WATER BOTTLE ☐ BLANKET
☐ TOWEL   ☐ BOLSTER PILLOW
☐ BLOCK   ☐ OTHER: _____

SOUND ACCOMPANIMENT: ☐ NO MUSIC   ☐ MUSIC

FAVORITE TRACK FROM TODAY'S SESSION
(TURN TO PAGE 20 AND ADD THE SONG TO YOUR YOGA SOUNDTRACK.)

Overall Session Rating

PACE OF FLOW: ①②③④⑤

FAVORITE POSE OF TODAY'S SESSION:

DYNAMISM OF SEQUENCING: ①②③④⑤

DIFFICULTY: ①②③④⑤

MOST CHALLENGING POSE:

POSES INCLUDED IN TODAY'S SEQUENCING:

☐ STANDING POSES   ☐ FORWARD BENDS
☐ BALANCING POSES   ☐ BACKBENDS
☐ SEATED POSES   ☐ INVERSIONS
☐ ABDOMINAL STRENGTHENERS ☐ RESTING POSES
☐ TWISTS

POSE YOU HADN'T TRIED BEFORE TODAY:

POSE IN WHICH YOU SHOWED THE MOST IMPROVEMENT:

POSE YOU'D LIKE TO WORK ON IN THE NEXT SESSION:

Dedication

Notes and Takeaways

Self-Review

One a scale of 1 to 5 (low to high), rate the following areas of your performance during this session:

FOCUS: ① ② ③ ④ ⑤

EVENNESS OF BREATH: ① ② ③ ④ ⑤

BALANCE: ① ② ③ ④ ⑤

STRENGTH: ① ② ③ ④ ⑤

ENERGY LEVEL: ① ② ③ ④ ⑤

ATTITUDE: ① ② ③ ④ ⑤

DATE   /   /   **TIME** START - FINISH

☐ **Group Class Practice**

☐ **Home Practice and/or Private Instruction**

NAME OF STUDIO: _____ (OR) IN WHAT ROOM/SPACE DID YOU PRACTICE?

NAME OF TEACHER: _____

TEACHER RATING (CIRCLE ONE): A+ A A- B C D F

CLASS LEVEL:

☐ BEGINNER   ☐ INTERMEDIATE   ☐ ADVANCED

CROWD LEVEL: ①②③④⑤
     NOT CROWDED ▸ CROWDED

TEMPERATURE: ☐ HEATED   ☐ UNHEATED

ON WHAT PART OF THE BODY DID YOU FOCUS DURING THIS SESSION?

☐ ABDOMINALS   ☐ HIPS
☐ BACK   ☐ BUTTOCKS
☐ SHOULDERS   ☐ LEGS
☐ ARMS   ☐ ANKLES/FEET
☐ WRISTS/HANDS   ☐ OTHER:

Session Details

WHAT STYLE DID YOU PRACTICE DURING THIS SESSION?

☐ ANUSARA   ☐ KRIPALU
☐ ASHTANGA   ☐ KUNDALINI
☐ BIKRAM   ☐ POWER
☐ IYENGAR   ☐ RESTORATIVE
☐ JIVAMUKTI   ☐ VINIYOGA
     ☐ OTHER:

WHAT TOOLS DID YOU HAVE ON HAND?

☐ MAT   ☐ STRAP
☐ WATER BOTTLE   ☐ BLANKET
☐ TOWEL   ☐ BOLSTER PILLOW
☐ BLOCK   ☐ OTHER:

SOUND ACCOMPANIMENT: ☐ NO MUSIC   ☐ MUSIC

FAVORITE TRACK FROM TODAY'S SESSION
(TURN TO PAGE 20 AND ADD THE SONG TO YOUR YOGA SOUNDTRACK.)

Overall Session Rating

PACE OF FLOW: ①②③④⑤

DYNAMISM OF SEQUENCING: ①②③④⑤

DIFFICULTY: ①②③④⑤

POSES INCLUDED IN TODAY'S SEQUENCING:

☐ STANDING POSES   ☐ FORWARD BENDS
☐ BALANCING POSES   ☐ BACKBENDS
☐ SEATED POSES   ☐ INVERSIONS
☐ ABDOMINAL STRENGTHENERS   ☐ RESTING POSES
☐ TWISTS

FAVORITE POSE OF TODAY'S SESSION:

MOST CHALLENGING POSE:

POSE YOU HADN'T TRIED BEFORE TODAY:

POSE IN WHICH YOU SHOWED THE MOST IMPROVEMENT:

POSE YOU'D LIKE TO WORK ON IN THE NEXT SESSION:

Dedication

Notes and Takeaways

Self-Review

One a scale of 1 to 5 (low to high), rate the following areas of your performance during this session:

FOCUS: ① ② ③ ④ ⑤

EVENNESS OF BREATH: ① ② ③ ④ ⑤

BALANCE: ① ② ③ ④ ⑤

STRENGTH: ① ② ③ ④ ⑤

ENERGY LEVEL: ① ② ③ ④ ⑤

ATTITUDE: ① ② ③ ④ ⑤

DATE / / **TIME** START - FINISH

☐ **Group Class Practice**

☐ **Home Practice and/or Private Instruction**

NAME OF STUDIO: (OR) IN WHAT ROOM/SPACE DID YOU PRACTICE?

NAME OF TEACHER:

TEACHER RATING (CIRCLE ONE): A+ A A- B C D F

ON WHAT PART OF THE BODY DID YOU FOCUS DURING THIS SESSION?

CLASS LEVEL:

☐ BEGINNER ☐ INTERMEDIATE ☐ ADVANCED

☐ ABDOMINALS ☐ HIPS

☐ BACK ☐ BUTTOCKS

CROWD LEVEL: ① ② ③ ④ ⑤

☐ SHOULDERS ☐ LEGS

NOT CROWDED ► CROWDED

☐ ARMS ☐ ANKLES/FEET

TEMPERATURE: ☐ HEATED ☐ UNHEATED

☐ WRISTS/HANDS ☐ OTHER:

Session Details

WHAT STYLE DID YOU PRACTICE DURING THIS SESSION?

☐ ANUSARA ☐ KRIPALU

☐ ASHTANGA ☐ KUNDALINI

☐ BIKRAM ☐ POWER

☐ IYENGAR ☐ RESTORATIVE

☐ JIVAMUKTI ☐ VINIYOGA

☐ OTHER:

WHAT TOOLS DID YOU HAVE ON HAND?

☐ MAT ☐ STRAP

☐ WATER BOTTLE ☐ BLANKET

☐ TOWEL ☐ BOLSTER PILLOW

☐ BLOCK ☐ OTHER:

SOUND ACCOMPANIMENT: ☐ NO MUSIC ☐ MUSIC

FAVORITE TRACK FROM TODAY'S SESSION

(TURN TO PAGE 20 AND ADD THE SONG TO YOUR YOGA SOUNDTRACK.)

Overall Session Rating

PACE OF FLOW: ① ② ③ ④ ⑤

FAVORITE POSE OF TODAY'S SESSION:

DYNAMISM OF SEQUENCING: ① ② ③ ④ ⑤

DIFFICULTY: ① ② ③ ④ ⑤

MOST CHALLENGING POSE:

POSES INCLUDED IN TODAY'S SEQUENCING:

POSE YOU HADN'T TRIED BEFORE TODAY:

☐ STANDING POSES ☐ FORWARD BENDS

☐ BALANCING POSES ☐ BACKBENDS

☐ SEATED POSES ☐ INVERSIONS

POSE IN WHICH YOU SHOWED THE MOST IMPROVEMENT:

☐ ABDOMINAL STRENGTHENERS ☐ RESTING POSES

☐ TWISTS

POSE YOU'D LIKE TO WORK ON IN THE NEXT SESSION:

Dedication

TO WHOM OR WHAT DID YOU DEDICATE THIS CLASS?

Notes and Takeaways

Self-Review

One a scale of 1 to 5 (low to high), rate the following areas of your performance during this session:

FOCUS: ①②③④⑤

EVENNESS OF BREATH: ①②③④⑤

BALANCE: ①②③④⑤

STRENGTH: ①②③④⑤

ENERGY LEVEL: ①②③④⑤

ATTITUDE: ①②③④⑤

DATE / / **TIME** START - FINISH

☐ **Group Class Practice**

☐ **Home Practice and/or Private Instruction**

NAME OF STUDIO: _____ (OR) IN WHAT ROOM/SPACE DID YOU PRACTICE?

NAME OF TEACHER: _____

TEACHER RATING (CIRCLE ONE): A+ A A- B C D F

ON WHAT PART OF THE BODY DID YOU FOCUS DURING THIS SESSION?

CLASS LEVEL:
☐ BEGINNER ☐ INTERMEDIATE ☐ ADVANCED

☐ ABDOMINALS ☐ HIPS
☐ BACK ☐ BUTTOCKS

CROWD LEVEL: (1)(2)(3)(4)(5)

NOT CROWDED ▸ CROWDED

☐ SHOULDERS ☐ LEGS
☐ ARMS ☐ ANKLES/FEET

TEMPERATURE: ☐ HEATED ☐ UNHEATED

☐ WRISTS/HANDS ☐ OTHER:

Session Details

WHAT STYLE DID YOU PRACTICE DURING THIS SESSION?

☐ ANUSARA ☐ KRIPALU
☐ ASHTANGA ☐ KUNDALINI
☐ BIKRAM ☐ POWER
☐ IYENGAR ☐ RESTORATIVE
☐ JIVAMUKTI ☐ VINIYOGA
☐ OTHER:

WHAT TOOLS DID YOU HAVE ON HAND?

☐ MAT ☐ STRAP
☐ WATER BOTTLE ☐ BLANKET
☐ TOWEL ☐ BOLSTER PILLOW
☐ BLOCK ☐ OTHER:

SOUND ACCOMPANIMENT: ☐ NO MUSIC ☐ MUSIC

FAVORITE TRACK FROM TODAY'S SESSION
(TURN TO PAGE 20 AND ADD THE SONG TO YOUR YOGA SOUNDTRACK.)

Overall Session Rating

PACE OF FLOW: (1)(2)(3)(4)(5)

DYNAMISM OF SEQUENCING: (1)(2)(3)(4)(5)

DIFFICULTY: (1)(2)(3)(4)(5)

FAVORITE POSE OF TODAY'S SESSION:

MOST CHALLENGING POSE:

POSES INCLUDED IN TODAY'S SEQUENCING:

☐ STANDING POSES ☐ FORWARD BENDS
☐ BALANCING POSES ☐ BACKBENDS
☐ SEATED POSES ☐ INVERSIONS
☐ ABDOMINAL STRENGTHENERS ☐ RESTING POSES
☐ TWISTS

POSE YOU HADN'T TRIED BEFORE TODAY:

POSE IN WHICH YOU SHOWED THE MOST IMPROVEMENT:

POSE YOU'D LIKE TO WORK ON IN THE NEXT SESSION:

Dedication

Notes and Takeaways

Self-Review

One a scale of 1 to 5 (low to high), rate the following areas of your performance during this session:

FOCUS: 1 2 3 4 5

EVENNESS OF BREATH: 1 2 3 4 5

BALANCE: 1 2 3 4 5

STRENGTH: 1 2 3 4 5

ENERGY LEVEL: 1 2 3 4 5

ATTITUDE: 1 2 3 4 5

DATE / / **TIME** START - FINISH

☐ Group Class Practice

(OR)

☐ Home Practice and/or Private Instruction

NAME OF STUDIO:

IN WHAT ROOM/SPACE DID YOU PRACTICE?

NAME OF TEACHER:

TEACHER RATING (CIRCLE ONE): A+ A A- B C D F

CLASS LEVEL:

ON WHAT PART OF THE BODY DID YOU FOCUS DURING THIS SESSION?

☐ BEGINNER ☐ INTERMEDIATE ☐ ADVANCED

CROWD LEVEL: ① ② ③ ④ ⑤

     NOT CROWDED ▸ CROWDED

TEMPERATURE: ☐ HEATED ☐ UNHEATED

☐ ABDOMINALS ☐ HIPS
☐ BACK ☐ BUTTOCKS
☐ SHOULDERS ☐ LEGS
☐ ARMS ☐ ANKLES/FEET
☐ WRISTS/HANDS ☐ OTHER:

Session Details

WHAT STYLE DID YOU PRACTICE DURING THIS SESSION?

☐ ANUSARA ☐ KRIPALU
☐ ASHTANGA ☐ KUNDALINI
☐ BIKRAM ☐ POWER
☐ IYENGAR ☐ RESTORATIVE
☐ JIVAMUKTI ☐ VINIYOGA
    ☐ OTHER:

WHAT TOOLS DID YOU HAVE ON HAND?

☐ MAT ☐ STRAP
☐ WATER BOTTLE ☐ BLANKET
☐ TOWEL ☐ BOLSTER PILLOW
☐ BLOCK ☐ OTHER:

SOUND ACCOMPANIMENT: ☐ NO MUSIC ☐ MUSIC

FAVORITE TRACK FROM TODAY'S SESSION

(TURN TO PAGE 20 AND ADD THE SONG TO YOUR YOGA SOUNDTRACK.)

Overall Session Rating

PACE OF FLOW: ① ② ③ ④ ⑤

DYNAMISM OF SEQUENCING: ① ② ③ ④ ⑤

DIFFICULTY: ① ② ③ ④ ⑤

FAVORITE POSE OF TODAY'S SESSION:

MOST CHALLENGING POSE:

POSES INCLUDED IN TODAY'S SEQUENCING:

☐ STANDING POSES ☐ FORWARD BENDS
☐ BALANCING POSES ☐ BACKBENDS
☐ SEATED POSES ☐ INVERSIONS
☐ ABDOMINAL STRENGTHENERS ☐ RESTING POSES
☐ TWISTS

POSE YOU HADN'T TRIED BEFORE TODAY:

POSE IN WHICH YOU SHOWED THE MOST IMPROVEMENT:

POSE YOU'D LIKE TO WORK ON IN THE NEXT SESSION:

Dedication

Notes and Takeaways

Self-Review

One a scale of 1 to 5 (low to high), rate the following areas of your performance during this session:

FOCUS: 1 2 3 4 5

EVENNESS OF BREATH: 1 2 3 4 5

BALANCE: 1 2 3 4 5

STRENGTH: 1 2 3 4 5

ENERGY LEVEL: 1 2 3 4 5

ATTITUDE: 1 2 3 4 5

DATE / / **TIME** START - FINISH

☐ **Group Class Practice**

☐ **Home Practice and/or Private Instruction**

NAME OF STUDIO: ....

(OR)

IN WHAT ROOM/SPACE DID YOU PRACTICE?

NAME OF TEACHER: ....

TEACHER RATING (CIRCLE ONE): A+ A A- B C D F

ON WHAT PART OF THE BODY DID YOU FOCUS DURING THIS SESSION?

CLASS LEVEL:

☐ BEGINNER ☐ INTERMEDIATE ☐ ADVANCED

☐ ABDOMINALS ☐ HIPS

☐ BACK ☐ BUTTOCKS

CROWD LEVEL: ①②③④⑤

☐ SHOULDERS ☐ LEGS

NOT CROWDED ▸ CROWDED

☐ ARMS ☐ ANKLES/FEET

TEMPERATURE: ☐ HEATED ☐ UNHEATED

☐ WRISTS/HANDS ☐ OTHER: ....

Session Details

WHAT STYLE DID YOU PRACTICE DURING THIS SESSION?

☐ ANUSARA ☐ KRIPALU

☐ ASHTANGA ☐ KUNDALINI

☐ BIKRAM ☐ POWER

☐ IYENGAR ☐ RESTORATIVE

☐ JIVAMUKTI ☐ VINIYOGA

☐ OTHER: ....

WHAT TOOLS DID YOU HAVE ON HAND?

☐ MAT ☐ STRAP

☐ WATER BOTTLE ☐ BLANKET

☐ TOWEL ☐ BOLSTER PILLOW

☐ BLOCK ☐ OTHER: ....

SOUND ACCOMPANIMENT: ☐ NO MUSIC ☐ MUSIC

FAVORITE TRACK FROM TODAY'S SESSION

(TURN TO PAGE 20 AND ADD THE SONG TO YOUR YOGA SOUNDTRACK.)

Overall Session Rating

PACE OF FLOW: ①②③④⑤

FAVORITE POSE OF TODAY'S SESSION:

DYNAMISM OF SEQUENCING: ①②③④⑤

DIFFICULTY: ①②③④⑤

MOST CHALLENGING POSE:

POSES INCLUDED IN TODAY'S SEQUENCING:

☐ STANDING POSES ☐ FORWARD BENDS

POSE YOU HADN'T TRIED BEFORE TODAY:

☐ BALANCING POSES ☐ BACKBENDS

☐ SEATED POSES ☐ INVERSIONS

POSE IN WHICH YOU SHOWED THE MOST IMPROVEMENT:

☐ ABDOMINAL STRENGTHENERS ☐ RESTING POSES

☐ TWISTS

POSE YOU'D LIKE TO WORK ON IN THE NEXT SESSION:

Dedication

Notes and Takeaways

Self-Review

One a scale of 1 to 5 (low to high), rate the following areas of your performance during this session:

FOCUS: ① ② ③ ④ ⑤

EVENNESS
OF BREATH: ① ② ③ ④ ⑤

BALANCE: ① ② ③ ④ ⑤

STRENGTH: ① ② ③ ④ ⑤

ENERGY
LEVEL: ① ② ③ ④ ⑤

ATTITUDE: ① ② ③ ④ ⑤

DATE / / **TIME** START - FINISH

☐ **Group Class Practice**

☐ **Home Practice and/or Private Instruction**

NAME OF STUDIO: _____ (OR) IN WHAT ROOM/SPACE DID YOU PRACTICE?

NAME OF TEACHER: _____

TEACHER RATING (CIRCLE ONE): A+ A A- B C D F

CLASS LEVEL:

☐ BEGINNER ☐ INTERMEDIATE ☐ ADVANCED

CROWD LEVEL: ①②③④⑤

NOT CROWDED ▸ CROWDED

TEMPERATURE: ☐ HEATED ☐ UNHEATED

ON WHAT PART OF THE BODY DID YOU FOCUS DURING THIS SESSION?

☐ ABDOMINALS ☐ HIPS
☐ BACK ☐ BUTTOCKS
☐ SHOULDERS ☐ LEGS
☐ ARMS ☐ ANKLES/FEET
☐ WRISTS/HANDS ☐ OTHER:

Session Details

WHAT STYLE DID YOU PRACTICE DURING THIS SESSION?

☐ ANUSARA ☐ KRIPALU
☐ ASHTANGA ☐ KUNDALINI
☐ BIKRAM ☐ POWER
☐ IYENGAR ☐ RESTORATIVE
☐ JIVAMUKTI ☐ VINIYOGA
☐ OTHER: _____

WHAT TOOLS DID YOU HAVE ON HAND?

☐ MAT ☐ STRAP
☐ WATER BOTTLE ☐ BLANKET
☐ TOWEL ☐ BOLSTER PILLOW
☐ BLOCK ☐ OTHER:

SOUND ACCOMPANIMENT: ☐ NO MUSIC ☐ MUSIC

FAVORITE TRACK FROM TODAY'S SESSION

(TURN TO PAGE 20 AND ADD THE SONG TO YOUR YOGA SOUNDTRACK.)

Overall Session Rating

PACE OF FLOW: ①②③④⑤

DYNAMISM OF SEQUENCING: ①②③④⑤

DIFFICULTY: ①②③④⑤

POSES INCLUDED IN TODAY'S SEQUENCING:

☐ STANDING POSES ☐ FORWARD BENDS
☐ BALANCING POSES ☐ BACKBENDS
☐ SEATED POSES ☐ INVERSIONS
☐ ABDOMINAL STRENGTHENERS ☐ RESTING POSES
☐ TWISTS

FAVORITE POSE OF TODAY'S SESSION:

MOST CHALLENGING POSE:

POSE YOU HADN'T TRIED BEFORE TODAY:

POSE IN WHICH YOU SHOWED THE MOST IMPROVEMENT:

POSE YOU'D LIKE TO WORK ON IN THE NEXT SESSION:

Dedication

TO WHOM OR WHAT DID YOU DEDICATE THIS CLASS?

Notes and Takeaways

Self-Review

One a scale of 1 to 5 (low to high), rate the following areas of your performance during this session:

FOCUS: 1 2 3 4 5

EVENNESS
OF BREATH: 1 2 3 4 5

BALANCE: 1 2 3 4 5

STRENGTH: 1 2 3 4 5

ENERGY
LEVEL: 1 2 3 4 5

ATTITUDE: 1 2 3 4 5

DATE   /   /   TIME   START - FINISH

☐ Group Class Practice

☐ Home Practice and/or Private Instruction

NAME OF STUDIO: _____

(OR)   IN WHAT ROOM/SPACE DID YOU PRACTICE?

NAME OF TEACHER: _____

TEACHER RATING (CIRCLE ONE): A+ A A- B C D F

CLASS LEVEL:

☐ BEGINNER   ☐ INTERMEDIATE   ☐ ADVANCED

CROWD LEVEL: (1)(2)(3)(4)(5)
             NOT CROWDED ▶ CROWDED

TEMPERATURE: ☐ HEATED   ☐ UNHEATED

ON WHAT PART OF THE BODY DID YOU FOCUS DURING THIS SESSION?

☐ ABDOMINALS   ☐ HIPS
☐ BACK   ☐ BUTTOCKS
☐ SHOULDERS   ☐ LEGS
☐ ARMS   ☐ ANKLES/FEET
☐ WRISTS/HANDS ☐ OTHER: _____

Session Details

WHAT STYLE DID YOU PRACTICE DURING THIS SESSION?

☐ ANUSARA   ☐ KRIPALU
☐ ASHTANGA   ☐ KUNDALINI
☐ BIKRAM   ☐ POWER
☐ IYENGAR   ☐ RESTORATIVE
☐ JIVAMUKTI   ☐ VINIYOGA
               ☐ OTHER: _____

WHAT TOOLS DID YOU HAVE ON HAND?

☐ MAT   ☐ STRAP
☐ WATER BOTTLE   ☐ BLANKET
☐ TOWEL   ☐ BOLSTER PILLOW
☐ BLOCK   ☐ OTHER: _____

SOUND ACCOMPANIMENT: ☐ NO MUSIC   ☐ MUSIC

FAVORITE TRACK FROM TODAY'S SESSION
(TURN TO PAGE 20 AND ADD THE SONG TO YOUR YOGA SOUNDTRACK.)

Overall Session Rating

PACE OF FLOW: (1)(2)(3)(4)(5)

DYNAMISM OF SEQUENCING: (1)(2)(3)(4)(5)

DIFFICULTY: (1)(2)(3)(4)(5)

POSES INCLUDED IN TODAY'S SEQUENCING:

☐ STANDING POSES   ☐ FORWARD BENDS
☐ BALANCING POSES   ☐ BACKBENDS
☐ SEATED POSES   ☐ INVERSIONS
☐ ABDOMINAL STRENGTHENERS   ☐ RESTING POSES
☐ TWISTS

FAVORITE POSE OF TODAY'S SESSION:

MOST CHALLENGING POSE:

POSE YOU HADN'T TRIED BEFORE TODAY:

POSE IN WHICH YOU SHOWED THE MOST IMPROVEMENT:

POSE YOU'D LIKE TO WORK ON IN THE NEXT SESSION:

Dedication

Notes and Takeaways

Self-Review

One a scale of 1 to 5 (low to high), rate the following areas of your performance during this session:

FOCUS: ①②③④⑤

EVENNESS OF BREATH: ①②③④⑤

BALANCE: ①②③④⑤

STRENGTH: ①②③④⑤

ENERGY LEVEL: ①②③④⑤

ATTITUDE: ①②③④⑤

DATE   /   /   TIME   START - FINISH

☐ **Group Class Practice**

NAME OF STUDIO: _____

NAME OF TEACHER: _____

TEACHER RATING (CIRCLE ONE): A+ A A- B C D F

CLASS LEVEL:

☐ BEGINNER   ☐ INTERMEDIATE   ☐ ADVANCED

CROWD LEVEL: ① ② ③ ④ ⑤

　　　　　　NOT CROWDED ▸ CROWDED

TEMPERATURE: ☐ HEATED   ☐ UNHEATED

(OR)

☐ **Home Practice and/or Private Instruction**

IN WHAT ROOM/SPACE DID YOU PRACTICE?

ON WHAT PART OF THE BODY DID YOU FOCUS DURING THIS SESSION?

☐ ABDOMINALS   ☐ HIPS
☐ BACK   ☐ BUTTOCKS
☐ SHOULDERS   ☐ LEGS
☐ ARMS   ☐ ANKLES/FEET
☐ WRISTS/HANDS   ☐ OTHER: _____

Session Details

WHAT STYLE DID YOU PRACTICE DURING THIS SESSION?

☐ ANUSARA   ☐ KRIPALU
☐ ASHTANGA   ☐ KUNDALINI
☐ BIKRAM   ☐ POWER
☐ IYENGAR   ☐ RESTORATIVE
☐ JIVAMUKTI   ☐ VINIYOGA
　　　　　　　　　　☐ OTHER: _____

WHAT TOOLS DID YOU HAVE ON HAND?

☐ MAT   ☐ STRAP
☐ WATER BOTTLE   ☐ BLANKET
☐ TOWEL   ☐ BOLSTER PILLOW
☐ BLOCK   ☐ OTHER: _____

SOUND ACCOMPANIMENT: ☐ NO MUSIC   ☐ MUSIC

FAVORITE TRACK FROM TODAY'S SESSION

(TURN TO PAGE 20 AND ADD THE SONG TO YOUR YOGA SOUNDTRACK.)

Overall Session Rating

PACE OF FLOW: ① ② ③ ④ ⑤

DYNAMISM OF SEQUENCING: ① ② ③ ④ ⑤

DIFFICULTY: ① ② ③ ④ ⑤

POSES INCLUDED IN TODAY'S SEQUENCING:

☐ STANDING POSES   ☐ FORWARD BENDS
☐ BALANCING POSES   ☐ BACKBENDS
☐ SEATED POSES   ☐ INVERSIONS
☐ ABDOMINAL STRENGTHENERS   ☐ RESTING POSES
☐ TWISTS

FAVORITE POSE OF TODAY'S SESSION:

MOST CHALLENGING POSE:

POSE YOU HADN'T TRIED BEFORE TODAY:

POSE IN WHICH YOU SHOWED THE MOST IMPROVEMENT:

POSE YOU'D LIKE TO WORK ON IN THE NEXT SESSION:

Dedication

....

TO WHOM OR WHAT DID YOU DEDICATE THIS CLASS?

Notes and Takeaways

Self-Review

One a scale of 1 to 5 (low to high), rate the following areas of your performance during this session:

FOCUS: (1)-(2)-(3)-(4)-(5)

EVENNESS OF BREATH: (1)-(2)-(3)-(4)-(5)

BALANCE: (1)-(2)-(3)-(4)-(5)

STRENGTH: (1)-(2)-(3)-(4)-(5)

ENERGY LEVEL: (1)-(2)-(3)-(4)-(5)

ATTITUDE: (1)-(2)-(3)-(4)-(5)

DATE   /   /   TIME   START - FINISH

☐ **Group Class Practice**

NAME OF STUDIO: _____

NAME OF TEACHER: _____

TEACHER RATING (CIRCLE ONE): A+ A A- B C D F

CLASS LEVEL:
☐ BEGINNER ☐ INTERMEDIATE ☐ ADVANCED

CROWD LEVEL: ①②③④⑤
            NOT CROWDED ▸ CROWDED

TEMPERATURE: ☐ HEATED ☐ UNHEATED

(OR)

☐ **Home Practice and/or Private Instruction**

IN WHAT ROOM/SPACE DID YOU PRACTICE?

ON WHAT PART OF THE BODY DID YOU FOCUS DURING THIS SESSION?

☐ ABDOMINALS ☐ HIPS
☐ BACK ☐ BUTTOCKS
☐ SHOULDERS ☐ LEGS
☐ ARMS ☐ ANKLES/FEET
☐ WRISTS/HANDS ☐ OTHER: _____

Session Details

WHAT STYLE DID YOU PRACTICE DURING THIS SESSION?

☐ ANUSARA ☐ KRIPALU
☐ ASHTANGA ☐ KUNDALINI
☐ BIKRAM ☐ POWER
☐ IYENGAR ☐ RESTORATIVE
☐ JIVAMUKTI ☐ VINIYOGA
☐ OTHER: _____

WHAT TOOLS DID YOU HAVE ON HAND?

☐ MAT ☐ STRAP
☐ WATER BOTTLE ☐ BLANKET
☐ TOWEL ☐ BOLSTER PILLOW
☐ BLOCK ☐ OTHER: _____

SOUND ACCOMPANIMENT: ☐ NO MUSIC ☐ MUSIC

FAVORITE TRACK FROM TODAY'S SESSION
(TURN TO PAGE 20 AND ADD THE SONG TO YOUR YOGA SOUNDTRACK.)

Overall Session Rating

PACE OF FLOW: ①②③④⑤

DYNAMISM OF SEQUENCING: ①②③④⑤

DIFFICULTY: ①②③④⑤

POSES INCLUDED IN TODAY'S SEQUENCING:

☐ STANDING POSES ☐ FORWARD BENDS
☐ BALANCING POSES ☐ BACKBENDS
☐ SEATED POSES ☐ INVERSIONS
☐ ABDOMINAL STRENGTHENERS ☐ RESTING POSES
☐ TWISTS

FAVORITE POSE OF TODAY'S SESSION:

MOST CHALLENGING POSE:

POSE YOU HADN'T TRIED BEFORE TODAY:

POSE IN WHICH YOU SHOWED THE MOST IMPROVEMENT:

POSE YOU'D LIKE TO WORK ON IN THE NEXT SESSION:

Dedication

TO WHOM OR WHAT DID YOU DEDICATE THIS CLASS?

Notes and Takeaways

Self-Review

One a scale of 1 to 5 (low to high), rate the following areas of your performance during this session:

FOCUS: 1 2 3 4 5

EVENNESS OF BREATH: 1 2 3 4 5

BALANCE: 1 2 3 4 5

STRENGTH: 1 2 3 4 5

ENERGY LEVEL: 1 2 3 4 5

ATTITUDE: 1 2 3 4 5

DATE   /   /   TIME   START - FINISH

☐ **Group Class Practice**

☐ **Home Practice and/or Private Instruction**

NAME OF STUDIO: _____

(OR) IN WHAT ROOM/SPACE DID YOU PRACTICE?

NAME OF TEACHER: _____

TEACHER RATING (CIRCLE ONE): A+ A A- B C D F

ON WHAT PART OF THE BODY DID YOU FOCUS DURING THIS SESSION?

CLASS LEVEL:

☐ BEGINNER ☐ INTERMEDIATE ☐ ADVANCED

☐ ABDOMINALS ☐ HIPS
☐ BACK ☐ BUTTOCKS

CROWD LEVEL: (1)(2)(3)(4)(5)

☐ SHOULDERS ☐ LEGS

NOT CROWDED ▸ CROWDED

☐ ARMS ☐ ANKLES/FEET

TEMPERATURE: ☐ HEATED ☐ UNHEATED

☐ WRISTS/HANDS ☐ OTHER: _____

Session Details

WHAT STYLE DID YOU PRACTICE DURING THIS SESSION?

☐ ANUSARA ☐ KRIPALU
☐ ASHTANGA ☐ KUNDALINI
☐ BIKRAM ☐ POWER
☐ IYENGAR ☐ RESTORATIVE
☐ JIVAMUKTI ☐ VINIYOGA
☐ OTHER: _____

WHAT TOOLS DID YOU HAVE ON HAND?

☐ MAT ☐ STRAP
☐ WATER BOTTLE ☐ BLANKET
☐ TOWEL ☐ BOLSTER PILLOW
☐ BLOCK ☐ OTHER: _____

SOUND ACCOMPANIMENT: ☐ NO MUSIC ☐ MUSIC

FAVORITE TRACK FROM TODAY'S SESSION

(TURN TO PAGE 20 AND ADD THE SONG TO YOUR YOGA SOUNDTRACK.)

Overall Session Rating

PACE OF FLOW: (1)(2)(3)(4)(5)

FAVORITE POSE OF TODAY'S SESSION:

DYNAMISM OF SEQUENCING: (1)(2)(3)(4)(5)

DIFFICULTY: (1)(2)(3)(4)(5)

MOST CHALLENGING POSE:

POSES INCLUDED IN TODAY'S SEQUENCING:

☐ STANDING POSES ☐ FORWARD BENDS
☐ BALANCING POSES ☐ BACKBENDS
☐ SEATED POSES ☐ INVERSIONS
☐ ABDOMINAL STRENGTHENERS ☐ RESTING POSES
☐ TWISTS

POSE YOU HADN'T TRIED BEFORE TODAY:

POSE IN WHICH YOU SHOWED THE MOST IMPROVEMENT:

POSE YOU'D LIKE TO WORK ON IN THE NEXT SESSION:

Dedication

Notes and Takeaways

Self-Review

One a scale of 1 to 5 (low to high), rate the following areas of your performance during this session:

FOCUS: ① ② ③ ④ ⑤

EVENNESS OF BREATH: ① ② ③ ④ ⑤

BALANCE: ① ② ③ ④ ⑤

STRENGTH: ① ② ③ ④ ⑤

ENERGY LEVEL: ① ② ③ ④ ⑤

ATTITUDE: ① ② ③ ④ ⑤

Yoga Session (28)

DATE   /   /   TIME   START - FINISH

☐ **Group Class Practice**

NAME OF STUDIO: _____

NAME OF TEACHER: _____

TEACHER RATING (CIRCLE ONE): A+ A A- B C D F

CLASS LEVEL:
☐ BEGINNER ☐ INTERMEDIATE ☐ ADVANCED

CROWD LEVEL: ①②③④⑤
         NOT CROWDED ► CROWDED

TEMPERATURE: ☐ HEATED ☐ UNHEATED

(OR)

☐ **Home Practice and/or Private Instruction**

IN WHAT ROOM/SPACE DID YOU PRACTICE?

_____

ON WHAT PART OF THE BODY DID YOU FOCUS DURING THIS SESSION?

☐ ABDOMINALS   ☐ HIPS
☐ BACK   ☐ BUTTOCKS
☐ SHOULDERS   ☐ LEGS
☐ ARMS   ☐ ANKLES/FEET
☐ WRISTS/HANDS ☐ OTHER:

Session Details

WHAT STYLE DID YOU PRACTICE DURING THIS SESSION?

☐ ANUSARA   ☐ KRIPALU
☐ ASHTANGA   ☐ KUNDALINI
☐ BIKRAM   ☐ POWER
☐ IYENGAR   ☐ RESTORATIVE
☐ JIVAMUKTI   ☐ VINIYOGA
               ☐ OTHER:

WHAT TOOLS DID YOU HAVE ON HAND?

☐ MAT   ☐ STRAP
☐ WATER BOTTLE   ☐ BLANKET
☐ TOWEL   ☐ BOLSTER PILLOW
☐ BLOCK   ☐ OTHER:

SOUND ACCOMPANIMENT: ☐ NO MUSIC ☐ MUSIC

FAVORITE TRACK FROM TODAY'S SESSION

(TURN TO PAGE 20 AND ADD THE SONG TO YOUR YOGA SOUNDTRACK.)

Overall Session Rating

PACE OF FLOW: ①②③④⑤

DYNAMISM OF SEQUENCING: ①②③④⑤

DIFFICULTY: ①②③④⑤

POSES INCLUDED IN TODAY'S SEQUENCING:

☐ STANDING POSES   ☐ FORWARD BENDS
☐ BALANCING POSES ☐ BACKBENDS
☐ SEATED POSES   ☐ INVERSIONS
☐ ABDOMINAL STRENGTHENERS ☐ RESTING POSES
☐ TWISTS

FAVORITE POSE OF TODAY'S SESSION:

MOST CHALLENGING POSE:

POSE YOU HADN'T TRIED BEFORE TODAY:

POSE IN WHICH YOU SHOWED THE MOST IMPROVEMENT:

POSE YOU'D LIKE TO WORK ON IN THE NEXT SESSION:

Dedication

Notes and Takeaways

Self-Review

One a scale of 1 to 5 (low to high), rate the following areas of your performance during this session:

FOCUS: ①②③④⑤

EVENNESS OF BREATH: ①②③④⑤

BALANCE: ①②③④⑤

STRENGTH: ①②③④⑤

ENERGY LEVEL: ①②③④⑤

ATTITUDE: ①②③④⑤

Yoga Session 29

DATE   /   /   TIME START - FINISH

☐ **Group Class Practice**

NAME OF STUDIO:

NAME OF TEACHER:

TEACHER RATING (CIRCLE ONE): A+ A A- B C D F

CLASS LEVEL:
☐ BEGINNER ☐ INTERMEDIATE ☐ ADVANCED

CROWD LEVEL: ①②③④⑤
NOT CROWDED ▸ CROWDED

TEMPERATURE: ☐ HEATED ☐ UNHEATED

OR

☐ **Home Practice and/or Private Instruction**

IN WHAT ROOM/SPACE DID YOU PRACTICE?

ON WHAT PART OF THE BODY DID YOU FOCUS DURING THIS SESSION?
☐ ABDOMINALS ☐ HIPS
☐ BACK ☐ BUTTOCKS
☐ SHOULDERS ☐ LEGS
☐ ARMS ☐ ANKLES/FEET
☐ WRISTS/HANDS ☐ OTHER:

Session Details

WHAT STYLE DID YOU PRACTICE DURING THIS SESSION?
☐ ANUSARA ☐ KRIPALU
☐ ASHTANGA ☐ KUNDALINI
☐ BIKRAM ☐ POWER
☐ IYENGAR ☐ RESTORATIVE
☐ JIVAMUKTI ☐ VINIYOGA
☐ OTHER:

WHAT TOOLS DID YOU HAVE ON HAND?
☐ MAT ☐ STRAP
☐ WATER BOTTLE ☐ BLANKET
☐ TOWEL ☐ BOLSTER PILLOW
☐ BLOCK ☐ OTHER:

SOUND ACCOMPANIMENT: ☐ NO MUSIC ☐ MUSIC

FAVORITE TRACK FROM TODAY'S SESSION
(TURN TO PAGE 20 AND ADD THE SONG TO YOUR YOGA SOUNDTRACK.)

Overall Session Rating

PACE OF FLOW: ①②③④⑤

DYNAMISM OF SEQUENCING: ①②③④⑤

DIFFICULTY: ①②③④⑤

POSES INCLUDED IN TODAY'S SEQUENCING:
☐ STANDING POSES ☐ FORWARD BENDS
☐ BALANCING POSES ☐ BACKBENDS
☐ SEATED POSES ☐ INVERSIONS
☐ ABDOMINAL STRENGTHENERS ☐ RESTING POSES
☐ TWISTS

FAVORITE POSE OF TODAY'S SESSION:

MOST CHALLENGING POSE:

POSE YOU HADN'T TRIED BEFORE TODAY:

POSE IN WHICH YOU SHOWED THE MOST IMPROVEMENT:

POSE YOU'D LIKE TO WORK ON IN THE NEXT SESSION:

Dedication

Notes and Takeaways

Self-Review

One a scale of 1 to 5 (low to high), rate the following areas of your performance during this session:

FOCUS: ① ② ③ ④ ⑤

EVENNESS OF BREATH: ① ② ③ ④ ⑤

BALANCE: ① ② ③ ④ ⑤

STRENGTH: ① ② ③ ④ ⑤

ENERGY LEVEL: ① ② ③ ④ ⑤

ATTITUDE: ① ② ③ ④ ⑤

DATE   /   /   **TIME** START - FINISH

☐ **Group Class Practice**   ☐ **Home Practice and/or Private Instruction**

NAME OF STUDIO: _____ (OR)   IN WHAT ROOM/SPACE DID YOU PRACTICE?

NAME OF TEACHER: _____

TEACHER RATING (CIRCLE ONE): A+ A A- B C D F   ON WHAT PART OF THE BODY DID YOU FOCUS DURING THIS SESSION?

CLASS LEVEL:
☐ BEGINNER ☐ INTERMEDIATE ☐ ADVANCED   ☐ ABDOMINALS   ☐ HIPS
                                              ☐ BACK   ☐ BUTTOCKS
CROWD LEVEL: ①②③④⑤   ☐ SHOULDERS   ☐ LEGS
              NOT CROWDED ▶ CROWDED   ☐ ARMS   ☐ ANKLES/FEET

TEMPERATURE: ☐ HEATED   ☐ UNHEATED   ☐ WRISTS/HANDS ☐ OTHER: _____

Session Details

WHAT STYLE DID YOU PRACTICE DURING THIS SESSION?   WHAT TOOLS DID YOU HAVE ON HAND?

☐ ANUSARA   ☐ KRIPALU   ☐ MAT   ☐ STRAP
☐ ASHTANGA   ☐ KUNDALINI   ☐ WATER BOTTLE   ☐ BLANKET
☐ BIKRAM   ☐ POWER   ☐ TOWEL   ☐ BOLSTER PILLOW
☐ IYENGAR   ☐ RESTORATIVE   ☐ BLOCK   ☐ OTHER: _____
☐ JIVAMUKTI   ☐ VINIYOGA
               ☐ OTHER: _____

SOUND ACCOMPANIMENT: ☐ NO MUSIC   ☐ MUSIC

FAVORITE TRACK FROM TODAY'S SESSION _____
(TURN TO PAGE 20 AND ADD THE SONG TO YOUR YOGA SOUNDTRACK.)

Overall Session Rating

PACE OF FLOW: ①②③④⑤   FAVORITE POSE OF TODAY'S SESSION:

DYNAMISM OF
SEQUENCING: ①②③④⑤

DIFFICULTY: ①②③④⑤   MOST CHALLENGING POSE:

POSES INCLUDED IN TODAY'S SEQUENCING: POSE YOU HADN'T TRIED BEFORE TODAY:

☐ STANDING POSES   ☐ FORWARD BENDS
☐ BALANCING POSES   ☐ BACKBENDS
☐ SEATED POSES   ☐ INVERSIONS   POSE IN WHICH YOU SHOWED THE MOST IMPROVEMENT:
☐ ABDOMINAL   ☐ RESTING POSES
  STRENGTHENERS
                                        POSE YOU'D LIKE TO WORK ON IN THE NEXT SESSION:
☐ TWISTS

Dedication

Notes and Takeaways

Self-Review

One a scale of 1 to 5 (low to high), rate the following areas of your performance during this session:

FOCUS: ① ② ③ ④ ⑤

EVENNESS OF BREATH: ① ② ③ ④ ⑤

BALANCE: ① ② ③ ④ ⑤

STRENGTH: ① ② ③ ④ ⑤

ENERGY LEVEL: ① ② ③ ④ ⑤

ATTITUDE: ① ② ③ ④ ⑤

Yoga
Reference
Guide

The Branches of Yoga

Whether it's rigorous exercise that opens one's heart, or music, or service to others, there's a branch of yoga for everyone.

Here are the modern forms of today's most relevant branches:

Bhakti Yoga: The Yoga of Devotion
Purpose: To develop a personal relationship with the divine, however one chooses to define it

Hatha Yoga: The Yoga of Physical Exercise
Purpose: To purify the body and mind through yoga poses

Jnana Yoga: The Yoga of Wisdom
Purpose: To seek and understand the truth

Karma Yoga: The Yoga of Service
Purpose: To selflessly help others

Mantra Yoga: The Yoga of Sound
Purpose: To focus the mind by repeating a chosen mantra or sound

Raja Yoga: The Yoga of Meditation
Purpose: To experience moments of peace and clarity through quiet contemplation

Yoga Styles

When yoga hit the West in the late nineteenth century, a natural evolution occurred. Teachers trained by Indian masters began taking what they had learned and making it their own. Some instructors opened schools that followed closely in their particular lineage, while others used their knowledge as a starting point to develop their own creative styles. These days, there's a wide range of yoga styles suited to all personalities and skill levels, with variations in speed, levels of exertion, purposes, benefits, and environment (such as temperature of the room and noise level, for example).

Today's most popular styles include:

· Anusara Yoga

· Ashtanga Yoga

· Bikram Yoga

· Iyengar Yoga

· Jivamukti Yoga

· Kripalu Yoga

· Kundalini Yoga

· Power Yoga

· Restorative Yoga

· Viniyoga

Anusara Yoga

Anusara yoga presents the idea that, when practiced with proper alignment and intention, the poses can help one connect with inner joy, creativity, playfulness, and one's full potential. Rather than focusing on what needs to be fixed or corrected, Anusara teachers focus on the thriving goodness within and around us and seek to help uncover each student's unique, innate beauty. Anusara's Universal Principles of Alignment, which incorporate yoga philosophy and physical alignment techniques, are applied to the teaching of each pose. Classes include an opening invocation, a heart-opening theme, a flowing sequence chosen from a selection of more than 250 poses, and a final relaxation period.

Ashtanga Yoga

Ashtanga yoga, founded by K. Pattabhi Jois (1915–2009), features flowing movements called *vinyasas* that connect breath with movement. When done correctly, the blood circulates freely, creating internal heat and sweating, which is believed to purify the body and calm the mind. Sometimes referred to as Ashtanga Vinyasa Yoga, this style follows a universal sequence that students gradually learn from their teacher as they progress in skill and ability. Classes open with Sun Salutations (see page 88), followed by standing poses, seated poses, backbends, inversions, and finally a relaxation pose. Flow yoga and vinyasa yoga are variations of Ashtanga yoga.

Bikram Yoga

Bikram yoga, founded by Bikram Choudhury (b. 1946), is a standardized series of twenty-six poses practiced in a room heated to 105°F/40°C. The heat is believed to release toxins, improve circulation, and loosen up muscles. Because of the heat, it's recommended that you dress lightly and bring a towel and a bottle of water. The practice starts and ends with breathing exercises and includes standing poses, backbends, seated poses, and twists. Each pose is done twice, and proceeds in a fixed order. It's often called Hot Yoga when there is some deviation from Bikram's prescribed sequence.

Iyengar Yoga

Iyengar yoga was founded by B.K.S. Iyengar (b. 1918), who considered the body to be a vehicle toward a spiritual path. This style emphasizes precise alignment, anatomy, and sequencing of the poses in a very specific order. Classes are conducted like an in-depth workshop, focusing on only a few poses, hands-on adjustments, and holding demonstrations in the center of the room. Iyengar yoga encourages the use of props like blocks, chairs, blankets, and bolsters to promote relaxation, proper alignment, and opening the body in a safe way. Those who are sensitive to injury, or are healing from a specific injury, find Iyengar useful because of the careful instructions, attention to body mechanics, and thoughtful modifications of the poses to suit individual needs and comfort preferences.

Jivamukti Yoga

Jivamukti yoga, founded in New York City by Sharon Gannon and David Life in 1986, is a rigorous form of flowing yoga. Energetic Jivamukti classes include Sun Salutations, poses, chanting, music, relaxation, and meditation. Some classes open with a theme that is woven throughout the class, and there is an emphasis on alignment and hands-on adjustment. Loosely translated from Sanskrit, *jivan mukti* means "liberation while living." The founders' philosophy centers around five tenets: kindness, devotion, meditation, music, and studying yoga scripture. They encourage practitioners to bring yoga philosophy off the mat and into their daily lives and to live in a kind and compassionate way.

Kripalu Yoga

Kripalu yoga was founded by Amrit Desai (b. 1932), a native of India who was inspired by Swami Kripalvananda (1913–1981), after whom the practice is named. With a focus on bringing awareness to poses, breathwork, and meditation, Kripalu yoga encourages healing, psychological growth, spirituality, and creativity. By focusing on staying in the present moment while on the mat, this style encourages deepening your spiritual attunement, self-awareness, and empathy. It combines a slow-moving yet challenging class with a meditative awareness. Kripalu employs an approach referred to as BRFWA: breathe, relax, feel, watch, and allow.

Kundalini Yoga

Kundalini yoga practices—including breathing, poses, hand positions, chanting, and meditation—are designed to awaken the latent energy that sits at the base of the spine so that one can experience a higher consciousness. The practices focus on balancing the glandular and nervous systems for physical, mental, and spiritual health. A chant often heard in a Kundalini yoga class is *Sat Nam*, which means "truth is my identity." Kundalini yoga, as inspired by Yogi Bhajan (1929–2004), encourages teachers and practitioners to wear white clothing to nourish light and divinity.

Power Yoga

Power yoga is an overarching term for an athletic style of yoga that is popular in a gym setting as well as in studios. Its roots are in Ashtanga yoga. Poses are linked together by a *chaturanga* (four-limbed staff) pose (see page 89), and movements flow swiftly for an often sweaty cardio workout, likely accompanied by upbeat music. Variations of Power yoga are Power Vinyasa, Power Vinyasa Flow, and Dynamic Yoga.

Restorative Yoga

Restorative yoga is designed to counter stress by triggering the parasympathetic nervous system, which calms the body and lowers heart rate and blood pressure. Restorative yoga poses often incorporate props such as bolsters, blocks, and blankets that completely support the body, allowing it to relax and drop deeply into a stress-free state. Each pose requires time for the practitioner to arrange the body and adjust props until they arrive in a position of complete comfort. Once there, they lie still for up to twenty minutes. Restorative yoga was popularized by Judith Hanson Lasater—a physical therapist, yoga teacher, and scholar—in the 1990s.

Viniyoga

Viniyoga is useful for all kinds of yogis and is often recommended for people with injuries or illness because it's highly adaptable to one's needs. The practice includes poses, breathwork, meditation, chanting, and other methods designed to transform the body and mind. In a Viniyoga class, one might move in and out of the same pose repeatedly, making slight modifications while also focusing on the breath. Viniyoga was shaped by Gary Kraftsow (b. 1955), who based the practice on the teachings of Krishnamacharya (1888–1989) and T.K.V. Desikachar (b. 1938).

What Is Hatha Yoga?

Hatha yoga refers specifically to the physical aspect of yoga. The word *hatha* in Saṇskrit means "force," which can describe the strengthening movements of the body during a yoga class. Historically, physical movement was just one small part of the larger yoga tradition, but today the physical exercises known as Hatha yoga are what many recognize as modern yoga. Classes described as "hatha" often blend a few different styles rather than emphasizing just one.

What Is Vinyasa Yoga?

Some modern yoga classes are referred to as "Vinyasa yoga," which means that poses are linked together with flowing movements and often linked to the breath. Vinyasa also refers to carefully thought-out sequencing, with one pose preparing the body for the next. Think of Vinyasa as a graceful dance, with the same moves being repeated continuously.

Illustrated Yoga Pose Directory

With hundreds of poses to choose from, a yoga practice is infinitely customizable for every skill level, personality, and wellness goal. Yoga poses can be the center of a fitness program or can be an occasional add-on. Individually or grouped together, they can target specific muscles and areas of the body. Strung together into dynamic sequences, they can provide a full-body workout. The following pages present a sampling of some of the most commonly taught yoga poses, ideal for mixing, matching, and modifying to suit anyone's wellness goals.

Sun Salutation

Yoga's classic Sun Salutation (*Surya Namaskar*, in Sanskrit) is a flowing sequence that awakens the body and mind. Do it two times briskly on each side, linking each movement with your breath, for an energizing way to greet the day.

1. Mountain Pose

2. Mountain Pose with Arms Up

3. Standing Forward Bend

4. Lunge (Left Leg Forward)

5. Plank Pose

6. Four-Limbed Staff Pose

7. Upward-Facing Dog

8. Downward-Facing Dog

9. Lunge (Right Leg Forward)

10. Standing Forward Bend

11. Mountain Pose with Arms Up

12. Mountain Pose

Sun Salutation (*Surya Namaskar*)

Sun Salutation Poses

MOUNTAIN POSE
TADASANA
(ta-DA-sah-nah)

MOUNTAIN POSE WITH ARMS UP

STANDING FORWARD BEND

LUNGE

PLANK POSE

FOUR-LIMBED STAFF POSE
CHATURANGA DANDASANA
(chat-ur-ANGA don-DAH-sah-nah)

UPWARD-FACING DOG
URDHVA MUKHA SVANASANA
(OOrd-va MOO-ka svan-AH-sah-nah)

DOWNWARD-FACING DOG
ADHO MUKHA SVANASANA
(ODD-ho MOO-ka svan-AH-sah-nah)

Standing Poses

CHAIR POSE (or FIERCE POSE)
UTKATASANA
(OOT-kah-TAH-sah-nah)

WARRIOR POSE I
VIRABHADRASANA I
(vee-rah-bah-DRAH-sah-nah)

WARRIOR POSE II
VIRABHADRASANA II
(vee-rah-bah-DRAH-sah-nah)

EXTENDED TRIANGLE POSE
UTTHITA TRIKONASANA
(oo-TEE-tah trik-cone-AH-sah-nah)

REVOLVED TRIANGLE POSE
PARIVRTTA TRIKONASANA
(pah-ree-VRIT-ah trik-cone-AH-sah-nah)

EXTENDED SIDE ANGLE POSE
UTTHITA PARSVAKONASANA
(oo-TEE-tah pars-vah-cone-AH-sah-nah)

Balancing Poses

TREE POSE
VRKSASANA
(vrik-SHAHS-ah-nah)

DANCER'S POSE
NATARAJASANA
(nah-tah-rah-JAHS-ah-nah)

EAGLE POSE
GARUDASANA
(gah-roo-DAH-sah-nah)

SIDE PLANK POSE
VASISTHASANA
(vah-see-STAHS-ah-nah)

HALF MOON POSE
ARDHA CHANDRASANA
(ARE-duh chan-DRAH-sah-nah)

Seated Poses, Twists, and Abdominal Strengtheners

STAFF POSE
DANDASANA
(dahn-DAH-sah-nah)

BOUND ANGLE POSE
BADDHA KONASANA
(BAH-dah cone-AH-sah-nah)

COW-FACE POSE
GOMUKHASANA
(GO-moo-KAH-sah-nah)

SEATED TWIST

FULL BOAT POSE
PARIPURNA NAVASANA
(pah-ree-POOR-nah nah-VAH-sah-nah)

Forward Bends and Hip Openers

SEATED FORWARD BEND
PASCHIMOTTANASANA
(PAH-she-mow-tahn-AH-sah-nah)

SEATED WIDE-LEGGED FORWARD BEND
UPAVISTHA KONASANA
(ooh-pah-VEE-stah cone-AH-sah-nah)

HEAD-TO-KNEE POSE
JANU SIRSASANA
(JAH-new shear-SHAH-sah-nah)

PIGEON POSE

Backbends

LOCUST POSE
SALABHASANA
(sha-lah-BAHS-ah-nah)

COBRA POSE
BHUJANGASANA
(boo-jahng-AH-sah-nah)

BOW POSE
DHANURASANA
(dahn-your-AHS-ah-nah)

BRIDGE POSE
SETU BANDHA SARVANGASANA
(set-oo BAHN-dah sar-vahn-GAH-sah-nah)

CAMEL POSE
USTRASANA
(oo-STRAS-ah-nah)

FISH POSE
MATSYASANA
(mats-YAS-ah-nah)

Inversions

LEGS UP THE WALL
VIPARITA KARANI
(vi-pa-REE-ta ka-RON-ee)

SHOULDER STAND
SARVANGASANA
(sar-van-GA-sah-nah)

Resting Poses

CHILD'S POSE
BALASANA
(bah-LAS-ah-nah)

CORPSE POSE
SAVASANA
(sha-VAS-ah-nah)

Notes